Basic Electromagnetism
and its Applications

TUTORIAL GUIDES IN ELECTRONIC ENGINEERING

Series editors
Professor G.G. Bloodworth, *University of York*
Professor A.P. Dorey, *University of Lancaster*
Professor J.K. Fidler, *Open University*

This series is aimed at first- and second-year undergraduate courses. Each text is complete in itself, although linked with others in the series. Where possible, the trend towards a 'systems' approach is acknowledged, but classical fundamental areas of study have not been excluded; neither has mathematics, although titles wholly devoted to mathematical topics have been eschewed in favour of including necessary mathematical concepts under appropriate applied headings. Worked examples feature prominently and indicate, where appropriate, a number of approaches to the same problem.

A format providing marginal notes has been adopted to allow the authors to include ideas and material to support the main text. These notes include references to standard mainstream texts and commentary on the applicability of solution methods, aimed particularly at covering points normally found difficult. Graded problems are provided at the end of each chapter, with answers at the end of the book.

1. Transistor Circuit Techniques: discrete and integrated — G.J. Ritchie
2. Feedback Circuits and Op. Amps — D.H. Horrocks
3. Pascal for Electronic Engineers — J. Attikiouzel
4. Computers and Microprocessors: components and systems — A.C. Downton
5. Telecommunication Principles — J.J. O'Reilly
6. Digital Logic Techniques: principles and practice — T.J. Stonham
7. Transducers and Interfacing: principles and techniques — B.R. Bannister and D.G. Whitehead
8. Signals and Systems: models and behaviour — M.L. Meade and C.R. Dillon
9. Basic Electromagnetism and its Applications — A.J. Compton
10. Electromagnetism for Electronic Engineers — R.G. Carter

Basic Electromagnetism and its Applications

A.J. Compton
Department of Electronics
The Hatfield Polytechnic

VNR
UK

Van Nostrand Reinhold (UK) Co. Ltd

To C. V. Burridge
who first taught me the need
to 'puzzle ideas out for yourself'

© 1986 A.J. Compton

First published in 1986 by
Van Nostrand Reinhold (UK) Co. Ltd
Molly Millars Lane, Wokingham, Berkshire, England

Typeset in Times 10 on 12pt by Colset Private Ltd,
Singapore

Printed and bound in Hong Kong

British Library Cataloguing in Publication Data

Compton, A.J.
    Basic electromagnetism and its
    applications. —— (Tutorial guides in
    electronic engineering, ISSN 0266-2620)
    1. Electromagnetism
    I. Title   II. Series
    537   QC760

    ISBN 0-442-31744-1

(ISSN 0266-2620)

Preface

I have tried in this book to introduce the basic concepts of electromagnetic field theory at a level suitable for students entering degree or higher diploma courses in electronics or subjects allied to it. Examples and applications have been drawn from areas such as instrumentation rather than machinery, as this was felt to be more apt for the majority of such readers.

Some students may have been following courses with a strong bias towards practical electronics and perhaps not advanced their understanding of the physics of electric and magnetic fields greatly since 'O' level or its equivalent. The book therefore does not assume that 'A' level physics has been studied. Students of BTEC courses or 'A' level subjects such as technology might also find the material useful.

At the other extreme, students who have achieved well on an 'A' level course will, it is hoped, find stimulating material in the applications discussed and in the marginal notes, which suggest further reading or comment on the deeper implications of the work.

In a relatively short book, few of the topics can be developed further than first year level, so this book has been written in close association with Dr Richard Carter, whose book *Electromagnetism for Electronic Engineers*, also in this series, represents a continuation of the ideas introduced here. There is an overlap between the two books and Dr Carter's book also starts from basics, so each can be studied independently if desired. *Electromagnetism for Electronic Engineers* develops the ideas at a faster rate than will be found here, however, and also in a different order, for reasons discussed in Chapter 1 of this book.

An attempt has been made to limit the number of books referred to in the marginal notes, and in the Bibliography those books referred to on several occasions have been indicated. However, if a particular example or topic is covered exceptionally well, this is mentioned even if that source is not referred to again.

In some cases, papers in journals have proved a useful source of practical applications, and readers are encouraged to use their library facilities to find them.

I am indebted to many people for their help in enabling this book to see the light of day. Manufacturers and other suppliers of illustrations have been acknowledged in the text. The publishers and my series editors, Professors Tony Dorey and Greville Bloodworth, have given their time and advice over several meetings to ensure the book fits in with the Tutorial Guides concept and particularly with *Electromagnetism for Electronic Engineers*. I am grateful to Richard Carter, the author of the latter, for reading my manuscript and supplying many helpful ideas. Several of my colleagues at Hatfield, particularly Jon Ling and Barry Dance, have also supplied comments and useful criticisms. I have given most of the examples to students on the Electrical Engineering BEng course here and would like to thank them for detecting ambiguities in the questions and errors in the answers, which I hope I have now corrected; also my son Matthew, who has read the early chapters from the point of view of an 'A' level student.

My thanks are due also to staff and technicians at Hatfield Polytechnic for help in using computer facilities for word-processing and producing the typescript.

Finally, my wife and children gave me continual support over several months of writing and consequent neglect of domestic duties; I would like to thank them publicly for their forbearance.

Contents

Preface   v

1 Introduction   1

Structure of the book   1
Understanding fields   2

2 Electrical conduction and currents   4

Current and charge   4
Conduction equations   5
Current as an example of flux   8
Models of electrical conduction   12
Resistive circuit components   13

3 Potential and the electric field   20

Potential (voltage) in a circuit   20
Electric field   23
Conduction and charge mobility   26
Potential and field in space   28
Acceleration of charged particles in an electric field   33

4 Charge and electric flux   36

Capacitance   36
Electric flux and permittivity   37
Calculations in electrostatics   45

5 Electric fields in materials   50

Polarization and dielectrics   50
Electrostatic force and energy   55
Capacitor design   63
Further applications   65

6 Magnetic flux and circuits   70

Electromagnetic induction   70
Magnetomotive force, flux and reluctance   72
Magnetic circuits   73

7 Magnetic vectors   77

Vector B and flux   77
Directional rules and Lenz' law   80
Magnetic scalar potential and vector H 84
Predicting magnetic fields   88

8   Inductance and magnetic materials   92

Self and mutual inductance   92
Air-cored inductors   94
Calculations in magnetism   95
Magnetization   97
Electromagnetic machinery   100
Some applications   103

9   Magnetic energy and force   107

Magnetic energy   107
Reluctance force   109
Permanent magnets   113
Force from the motor effect   114

10   Electromagnetism and charged particles   119

The Lorentz force   119
The Hall effect   119
Applications of the Hall effect   122
Electron streams   125
Acceleration of electrons   126
Deflection and focusing of electron streams   126
Some applications of electron streams   131

11   The electromagnetic field   136

The time needed to establish a current   136
Electromagnetic waves   139
Electromagnetism and relativity   141
Final comments   142
The fundamental rules of electromagnetism   143

Appendix: A brief note on integration   144

Answers to problems   146

Bibliography   148

Index   149

Introduction

Structure of the Book

Chapter 2 carries out a survey of electrical conduction, covering the basic ideas of charge flow and resistance. It illustrates conduction processes with examples of different resistor construction and the properties of some resistive transducers. Current in a bulk medium is studied as an example of flow, or flux, to serve as a basis for understanding the ideas of electric and magnetic flux later.

Chapter 3 deals with potential, first associated with a point in a circuit, then enlarged to cover electrostatic situations, where no charge flows, but would if present and able to. The concept of an electric field is introduced, as the force on a test charge, and connected with the potential gradient setting up the field. Conduction in gases is studied more carefully, using field ideas, and practical examples of gas discharge are discussed.

In Chapter 4, the charge producing an electric field is introduced, via the concept of capacitance. The electric flux model is shown to be useful in solving problems and enlarging the study of electrostatics to include insulating materials. Methods of carrying out calculations are introduced also.

These ideas are developed further in Chapter 5, covering some practical applications of electrostatics.

Chapter 6 begins the study of magnetic fields using flux Φ as the starting point, defined from voltages induced when it changes. The concept of the magnetic circuit follows, with its associated ideas of magnetomotive force m.m.f. and reluctance S, and similarities to electric circuits are noted.

The magnetic vector B, as force on a current, appears in Chapter 7 and is shown to be equal to flux density. The idea is extended to the force on a moving charged particle, and this is shown to explain both the motor and dynamo effects at a fundamental level. Calculations involving B show up the usefulness of the magnetic scalar potential U and its gradient H as aids in solving problems.

Chapter 8 covers the practical application of magnetic field ideas to fixed components, that is inductors and transformers, and the properties of magnetic materials are described. Some important principles of electrical machinery design are also introduced.

The general properties of magnetic fields are concluded in Chapter 9, which looks at the forces and energy associated with them, applying the ideas to simple actuators and to magnets.

In the last two chapters, some important examples are discussed where electric and magnetic fields interact, either in materials or in space. Chapter 10 deals with the Hall effect and with electron streams and their dynamics. Finally, a brief introduction to the electromagnetic field is given in Chapter 11, culminating in an intuitive look at electromagnetic waves.

The author hopes that with the intuitive understanding he has attempted to foster in the reader, and some familiarity with the notation and mathematics used to describe fields, more advanced work can be tackled with confidence.

Understanding fields

When beginning work on field theory, the student usually has two related difficulties to contend with:

(a) what is real, and what is invention? Does the electric field E exist while the flux density D is but a figment of the author's imagination?

(b) which are the fundamental ideas of field theory? Is B in some sense more basic than H?

A rapid survey of library shelves or a bookshop may suggest that no-one knows the solution to (a), and no-one can agree on the right answer to (b).

The answer in both cases is more encouraging but more complex than this, and relies on knowing a little history, and something of what understanding means.

Taking the latter problem first:

A scientist or engineer meeting a new idea or phenomenon needs to ask questions on two levels:

A. Can I picture this new phenomenon intuitively?

B. Can I predict exactly what will happen when something affects it?

When you think of molecules as ball-bearings, or electric current in a wire as glowing dots moving along inside a tube, you are using level A. What you visualize inside your head is for your own consumption alone and doesn't need to be like anyone else's picture. It is sometimes called an internal or intuitive 'model'. Its most important property is that it enables you to imagine what is happening and follow, or perhaps predict, what happens in other circumstances. It usually helps you to understand a mathematical description better.

We use intuitive models a great deal. Some have become so popular and ingrained in our imaginations that they have taken on the trappings of reality. Electric and magnetic flux lines are good examples. They are generally accepted intuitive models for phenomena otherwise described only in mathematical terms. As Chapter 11 will mention, magnetic fields can be explained by charge, motion and relativity, but fields are much easier concepts to work with. For instance, the magnetic field produced by steady currents can be regarded as fixed in space; relativity would generate complex equations that represent the way delayed forces would act on a charge being affected by the motion of other charges forming those steady currents!

Whether electric fields as such exist could lead to ideas about what reality is (is it all an intuitive model?!) and will be pursued no further in a book not aimed at philosophers!

Taking level B now: communication with other people will either be in terms of mathematics or a generally accepted intuitive model, itself described mathematically. Magnetic flux is a good example of this. People visualize it as whiskers or tubes or lines or whatever, but also described it using equations like

$$V = -N\,\frac{d\Phi}{dt}$$

which represents the voltage V induced by flux Φ changing at a particular rate in a coil of N turns. Using this equation as a start, complex magnetic machines can be designed in which fields are changing in ways difficult for even the most expert engineer to visualize.

As you study this subject, you will need keep your knowledge of equations in step with your ability to visualize what fields are doing, as far as you can.

Back to the history problem.

In the early nineteenth century, magnetism, electrostatics and current electricity followed separate paths until current was shown to be a flow of charge, magnetism and currents could be made to interact and a combination of electric and magnetic fields could generate waves. Finally, Einstein demonstrated that magnetism is but relativity applied to moving electric charges. As a result of this:

(a) three separate, though dependent, systems of units were in operation until fairly recently and references to magnetic fields in 'gauss' can still be seen in the literature and in manufacturers' catalogues;

(b) no-one is agreed on where to start! some books begin with electrostatics, some with currents; historically, the fundamental electrical definitions have changed from the use of chemicals to forces and even quantities originally regarded as determined experimentally are now given defined values!

The force between two charges is fundamental, but is mathematically very difficult in most real cases; both electric and magnetic fields are more easily visualized models of real life, with the added bonus that their mathematics is far more straightforward.

It is perhaps best to stand outside this turmoil, and see electromagnetism as one large intuitive model that has been given mathematical expression and that predicts excellently what happens when the model impinges on the real world. Definitions can lead to results and other definitions, but no starting place is really fundamental in nature, only in our minds. Electric and magnetic fields form a complex but circular argument.

Because of this, the author makes no apology for beginning not with topics usually regarded as fundamental, but with those that are conceptually and mathematically straightforward, electric fields with force on a charge and magnetism with the magnetic circuit. These starting points are not to be regarded as physically any more fundamental than any other.

Now read on!

2 Electrical Conduction and Currents

Objectives

☐ To revise the basic properties of electric charge and current.
☐ To relate mathematically electric current to the flow of charge.
☐ To revise voltage and Ohm's law, and to introduce resistivity and conductivity.
☐ To introduce current flux and flux density and to derive equations relating them.
☐ To describe conduction processes in gases, liquids and solids.
☐ To show how resistors and resistive transducers represent applications of the principles covered earlier in the chapter.

Current and Charge

Electric charge is not easy to visualize. In spite of this, we can predict with great accuracy what it will do in any real situation, from a few basic properties:

The neutron (uncharged, heavy) is just as common, but contributes nothing to the electrical properties of materials at the level dealt with in this book.

(a) Charge exists in two forms, called positive and negative, which can appear on otherwise identical particles and cause them to respond as described below. Such particles are called the 'fundamental charge particles'. The most common by far are protons, which have a positive charge and are relatively heavy, and electrons, which are negatively charged and light.

The definitions + and − are an accident of history; Benjamin Franklin just happened to say glass became '+' when rubbed with flannel; we would now say that negative electrons had been removed.

(b) 'Uncharged' bulk material contains equal amounts of positive and negative charge. Electrons are readily removed from many materials and can be transferred easily to other objects.

Charged objects have a slight excess or deficiency of these negatively charged electrons, which may be regarded as the basic unit or quantum of charge. The size of the electron charge is -1.6×10^{-19} C (coulomb).

(c) When a charge interacts with another charge, each one feels an equal and opposite force in the following way:
   (i) Like charges repel, unlike attract and, in addition:
   (ii) Like charges moving in the same direction attract, in opposite directions repel, and vice versa for unlike charges.
   (i) is described as electrostatic behaviour, as it is most readily observed when no charge is flowing. (ii) can be explained by special relativity, but electromagnetism is a more convenient and mathematically easier way of describing it.

Chapters 1 and 11 discuss this.

(d) When charge flows, it becomes an electric current, as simple experiments like those in Fig. 2.1 show.

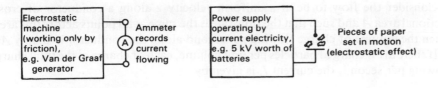

Fig. 2.1 Experiments showing identity of current and charge flow.

For an electric current to exist, in other words for conduction to take place, charge must be free to move.

Simple current measurements cannot show whether it is positive or negative charge, or even both together, which flows in any given conductor. A cell or battery can be made 'flat' by connecting it into a circuit so that either:

Later notes on electrolytes give examples of this.

(a) + charge flows from its + terminal to its − terminal;
(b) − charge flows from its − terminal to its + terminal;
(c) both (a) and (b) occur simultaneously.

Only Hall effect measurements can show what really happens, as will be made clear in Chapter 10.

Unit of charge

The unit of current, the ampere, is defined from its electromagnetic effect. The unit of charge, the coulomb, is defined as the charge passed when one ampere flows for one second.

C.A. Coulomb first measured the force between charged objects in 1785.

To allow for varying currents, this is expressed as

Notes on integration are contained in the Appendix.

$$\text{Charge passed } Q = \int I dt \qquad \text{where } I \text{ is current and } t \text{ time} \qquad (2.1)$$

$$= It \qquad \text{under constant conditions} \qquad (2.2)$$

Calculate the charge flowing to earth when a lightning flash occurs carrying an average current of 10kA for 80 μs.
(Answer: charge = 0.8 C)

Exercise 2.1

Conduction Equations

Current and charge flow

Eqn (2.1) can be differentiated to relate current to the charge flow producing it:

$$I = dQ/dt \qquad (2.3)$$

$$\text{average current} = Q/t \qquad (2.4)$$

where charge Q flows for time t

If the details of charge flow are to be considered, the equations need expanding to bring in the size of the charge unit flowing, usually one electron-charge q_e, its density or number of them in unit volume and its drift velocity in the direction of current flow.

5

Consider the flow to be at a uniform velocity v along a conductor of cross-sectional area A and such that the flow rate is the same at all points across this area. Then the volume of charge flowing per second along the conductor is simply Av.

If there are n charged particles per unit volume, each of charge q, the total charge flowing per second, the current I, is given by

$$I = nqAv \qquad (2.5)$$

If only the density of charge in coulomb metre^{-3} is known, not its nature, then

$$I = \rho Av \qquad (2.6)$$

where ρ (rho) is the charge density.

Worked Example 2.1

Calculate the speed of electrons in a copper wire of cross-sectional area 2.5 mm^2 (the usual domestic ring-main size) carrying a current of 13 A. The volume density of copper atoms in the wire is 8.5×10^{28} m^{-3}, and the charge on the electron is 1.6×10^{-19} C. Assume each atom contributes 1 electron for conduction.

Solution: This is a very straightforward example, requiring mere substitution in an equation, but the result may surprise you, if you have never calculated electron speeds in a wire before.

Rearranging Eqn (2.5) (which would need quoting in a proper answer, of course) to make velocity v the subject:

$$v = I/nqA$$

Substituting the quantities given in the question:

$$v = 13/(8.5 \times 10^{-28} \times 1.6 \times 10^{-19} \times 2.5 \times 10^{-6})$$
$$= 3.8 \times 10^{-4} \text{ m s}^{-1}, \text{ which is less than 1 mm s}^{-1}!$$

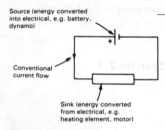

Source (energy converted into electrical, e.g. battery, dynamo)

Conventional current flow

Sink (energy converted from electrical, e.g. heating element, motor)

Resistance and conductance

We assumed above that charge flow or current was occurring, but made no mention of its cause. However, you will know that to obtain a steady current, a circuit including an energy source must be completed. Such a source generates an electromotive force (e.m.f.).

The energy given to every coulomb of charge passing through the source is called the **terminal voltage**, V, of the source. Voltage, charge Q and energy W are thus related by:

$$W = VQ \qquad (2.7)$$

If the energy flow rate or power P is important, it can be related from Eqn (2.7) to the charge flow rate or current I:

$$P = VI \qquad (2.8)$$

In Chapter 3 you will find an intuitive model of voltage, but for now voltage will be regarded simply as an equivalent 'number of cells in series'.

If the source above is made up of real cells in series, then if the number of cells is increased it is found experimentally that the current through the circuit becomes larger also. In some situations, the relationship between the current and the number of cells, or applied voltage, is non-linear and complex. However, for most materials and under conditions when the current is low enough to cause no measureable temperature rise, this current is found to be directly proportional to the number of cells. This is Ohm's law which can be expressed, like any other proportionality, as a constant ratio:

$$\frac{\text{applied voltage, } V}{\text{resulting current, } I} \text{ is constant for an 'ohmic' material}$$

$R = V/I$ is sometimes called Ohm's law, but his law simply states that R is a constant under certain conditions. $R = V/I$ is better referred to as Ohm's equation. Ohm's law is shown to follow from solid-state behaviour in Solymar in Walsh, chapter 1.

The ratio is called **resistance**, R, when expressed as V/I, which shows how hard it is for voltage to drive current, and **conductance**, G, when expressed as I/V, which shows how easy it is: the bigger the conductance, the larger is I for a given V.

This is an example of the semi-mathematical relationship: ease = 1/difficulty.

The units are, respectively, ohms (volt ampere^{-1}) and siemens (amp volt^{-1}), though the older 'mho' is still used for the latter.

In summary:

$$R = V/I \quad \text{ohms}(\Omega) \tag{2.9}$$

$$G = I/V \quad \text{siemens}(S) \tag{2.10}$$

Resistivity and conductivity

When comparing the electrical performance of different materials, a number is needed, different for each material, to work out the resistance or conductance in any particular application.

Consider charge flow along the axis of a rod, assuming uniform current flux across the area.

By experiment, the resistance V/I is found to be proportional to length l and inversely proportional to cross-sectional area A. This makes sense intuitively, as increasing l makes it harder to push current through, whereas increasing A is the same as providing alternative parallel paths for the current, making the overall current flow easier.

This can be expressed by two equivalent equations:

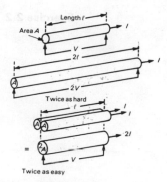

$$V/I = \rho l/A \tag{2.11}$$

$$= l/\sigma A \tag{2.12}$$

These differ only in the positions of the constants and the names given to them. ρ is called **resistivity**, σ (sigma) **conductivity** and they are related in the same reciprocal way as resistance and conductance.

The units of ρ can, by rearranging Eqn (2.11), be seen to be Ω m, whereas those of σ are S m^{-1}. ρ is sometimes described as 'the resistance of a one metre cube' (NOT of 1 m³), but remember the resistance value depends on the shape of the conductor as well as its volume.

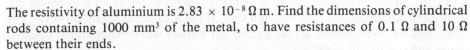

The resistivity of aluminium is $2.83 \times 10^{-8} \Omega$ m. Find the dimensions of cylindrical rods containing 1000 mm³ of the metal, to have resistances of 0.1 Ω and 10 Ω between their ends.

Worked Example 2.2

Solution: Though it would have limited practical application, this should make is clear that a given volume of material can provide a wide choice of resistance values.

Two equations will be needed, one using the resistivity and resistance data, the other bringing in the constancy of volume. Eqn (2.11) provides the first, the second will be that the volume

$$v = Al$$

Eliminating one quantity, say A, from these two:

$$A = v/l \quad \text{so} \quad R = \rho l^2/v$$

$$\text{Thus} \quad l = \sqrt{(Rv/\rho)}$$
$$= \sqrt{(0.1 \times 10^{-6}/2.83 \times 10^{-8})}$$
$$= 1.88 \text{ m}$$

$$\text{Hence } A = v/l = 5.32 \times 10^{-7} \text{ m}^2$$
$$\text{Hence diameter} = \sqrt{(4A/\pi)} = 0.82 \text{ mm}$$

This is a useful method of working when several answers are required from the same group of equations, and can often save time; it does demand a good intuitive grasp of the problem, however.

The calculations could simply be repeated for a resistance of 10 Ω, but l is proportional to $\sqrt{R}$, so for 10 Ω (that is, 100 times bigger):

$$l = 1.88 \times \sqrt{100} = 18.8 \text{ m}$$

l is thus 10 times bigger, so for the same volume A must be 10 times smaller, thus:

$$A = 5.32 \times 10^{-8} \text{ m}^2$$

and the diameter will be $\sqrt{10}$ times smaller, that is 0.26 mm.

Exercise 2.2   Calculate the length of 0.5 mm diameter nichrome wire needed to make a 1 kW heater to run off the 240 V mains supply. ρ for nichrome is 10^{-6} Ωm.
(Answer: length = 11.3 m, which would be coiled up, of course.)

Current as an Example of Flux

Current density

On several occasions we have needed to specify that current flow was uniform within a conducting rod. This idea will now be developed further to introduce a method of describing non-uniform situations.

It is now convenient to define a term **flux** for the amount of current flowing through a specified area.

If current flux is uniform across an area, it means that if smaller areas of the same size were defined within the larger area, the flux through each would be the same, wherever these smaller areas were taken. If the flux were non-uniform across the area, it could be different through each small area.

If we wished to determine the flux at some specified point in this non-uniform flow, there would be a problem. The flux at a point must be zero, as a point has zero area through which current can flow! Clearly, we must define an area round the point, and talk about the flux through that. If the area is not small, however, the flux could be non-uniform across it, and our answer will depend on the detailed shape and size of this area.

We have to take an infinitesimal area, therefore, which by definition is so small that no variation can be detected across it. Even so, the current flux through it may not be very helpful, as it still depends on the size of this tiny area. If, however, the current per unit area is considered, this will not depend on the actual dimensions.

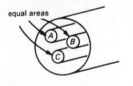
equal areas

Currents in A,B,C equal if flow uniform across whole area.

We can in principle shrink the area down to nothing, yet the current per unit area will still have meaning.

This quantity is called **current flux density**, J, and can have a finite value at a point within a conductor. It will clearly have units of A m^{-2}. If flow or flux lines are drawn within the conductor, J is represented by their density or closeness over any small region.

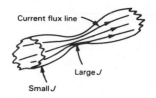

We shall find in Chapter 3 that J is the material's response as a conductor to the electric field at that point.

Vector equations for current flow

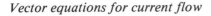

If the current flux I is uniform across the area A, it is easily related to the current density J:

$$I = JA \qquad (2.13)$$

If the flux is not uniform, we need again to consider tiny areas within the cross-section. This time we need the contribution the flux through each area dA makes to the total current. It will clearly be $J dA$, where J is the current density at dA. To find the total current means integrating over an entire cross-section, so the general expression for current flux through an area at right-angles to the flux direction is:

$$I = \iint J dA \qquad (2.14)$$

Finally, we may need to calculate the total flux through an area that is not plane, perhaps at a complex shaped interface between materials in an integrated circuit. Figure 2.2 shows an example.

S is often used rather than *A* as the symbol for area, to avoid confusion in more advanced work with a quantity called magnetic vector potential, *A*. Unfortunately, if care is not taken with writing and printing case, *S* can be confused with *s*, used for displacement along a (not necessarily straight) path. We use *l* for the latter.

The Appendix contains some notes on integration, including a discussion of the double integral sign.

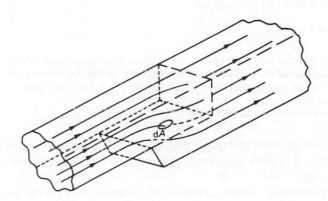

Fig. 2.2 Example of flux through a surface *not* at right angles.

In this case an area dA may not be normal to the current flux. A particular value of J will produce a smaller net current through dA than would be the case for normal incidence. The resulting current will therefore depend on the angle between the direction of current flux, in other words the direction of J, and the 'direction' of the area.

The latter needs defining carefully. Clearly, it cannot be a direction within the plane of the area, as there are an infinite number of those. A plane area has one unique direction, however, that of the normal to its surface. Fig. 2.3 illustrates, the

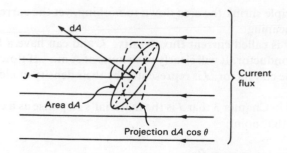

Fig. 2.3   Flux striking an area dA at an angle θ.

area 'seen' by the flux passing through dA is the projection of dA on to a plane normal to the flux. The area of this projection will be d$A \cos \Theta$.

The general expression for current flux dI through dA is, therefore:

$$dI = JdA \cos \Theta \qquad (2.15)$$

Expressions of this type occur frequently, and a shorthand notation called a **scalar** or **dot product of vectors** has been devised. The equation is written as:

$$dI = \mathbf{J.dA} \qquad (2.16)$$

This means 'To obtain dI find the angle between vectors $\mathbf{J}$ and $\mathbf{dA}$, then multiply the cosine of that angle by the product of the magnitudes of $\mathbf{J}$ and $\mathbf{dA}$'.

Finally, to allow the total flux I over an area to be found, all the small quantities dI need to be added, by integration:

$$I = \iint \mathbf{J.dA} \qquad (2.17)$$

Exercise 2.3   Lightning strikes a tree and a current of 5 kA flows into the ground, which is level. If the earth can be considered to be of uniform conductivity, so the current spreads into it radially from the base of the trunk, calculate the current density 2.5 m away from the base. Ignore the diameter of the trunk.
(Answer: current density = 127 A m^{-2})

We are now in a position to express mathematically Kirchhoff's first law (current conservation) as it applies to currents distributed within a conductor or under any conditions at all.

If the surface through which current flows is closed, then the net current flowing out of the surface is zero. This can be neatly written, for steady currents, as:

$$\oiint \mathbf{J.dA} = 0 \qquad (2.18)$$

where $\oiint$ represents integration over an enclosed surface.

Some authors write $\oiint J.dA = \Sigma I$ to represent the situation where wires lead current into or out of the volume enclosed by the surface, but if $\oiint$ represents total enclosure, this must include the wires! If charge is being temporarily stored in or removed from a volume, then $\oiint J.dA = -dQ/dt$.

One of the problems in the mathematical description of flux fields is that the equations produced look deceptively simple, but until you are used to them prove awkward to deal with. Examples are set in this chapter, but they must be simple almost to the point of triviality to allow them to be solved. However, they are the bases for more advanced work, and it was thought better to introduce them gently, coupled with plenty of intuitive ideas, so that they are more familiar when met later. Avoid simply memorizing these equations; have a picture in your mind when

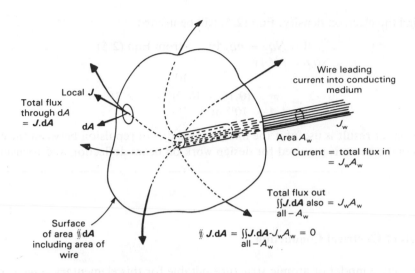

Fig. 2.4 Current flux through a totally enclosed surface.

you see and use them. For Eqn (2.18), for instance, think of current going into and out of a region of space, and adding it all up as shown in Fig. 2.4.

Electrons are emitted from a hot oxide surface at an average current density of 10^6 A m^{-2} in an electron gun. The electron optics can use 6% of these, bringing them to a circular focus 0.3 mm diameter on a screen. Calculate the oxide area required and the electron density within the beam if 6×10^{15} electrons per second are to arrive at the focused point at a velocity of 6×10^7 ms^{-1}. Assume in all cases that electron flux is perpendicular to area. The charge on one electron q_e is 1.6×10^{-19} C.

Solution: We shall meet electron guns in Chapter 10, but for now regard the example as a disguised problem in which current flux through one area flows also through another one, and that conservation of current is to be used.

We shall need to combine Eqns (2.4) and (2.5), concerning charged particle flow with Eqn (2.17), which involves current density. The latter can be immediately simplified to Eqn (2.13) as only average densities are involved, and all flux directions are assumed normal to areas.

Using other symbols as they appear in the equations to be used:

Current leaving oxide $\quad I = JA \quad$ from Eqn (2.13)

Of this, 6% arrives at the screen, so

$$0.06JA = Q/t \quad \text{from Eqn (2.4)}$$
$$= Nq_e$$

All quantities are known excepting A so

$$\text{oxide area } A = Nq_e/0.06J$$
$$= \frac{6 \times 10^{15} \times 1.6 \times 10^{-19}}{0.06 \times 10^6}$$
$$= 1.6 \times 10^{-8} \text{ m}^2 \text{ (16 mm}^2)$$

Worked Example 2.3

Note that the required number of electrons N arriving per second is not the same as n in Eqn(2.5).

To find the electron density, Eqn (2.5) will be needed:

$$I = Nq_e = nq_e Av \qquad \text{from Eqn (2.5)}$$
$$\text{so } n = N/Av$$
$$= \frac{6 \times 10^{15}}{\pi \times (0.15 \times 10^{-3})^2 \times 6 \times 10^7}$$
$$= 1.4 \times 10^{15} \text{ m}^{-3}$$

The latter result is useful if the likely spread due to repulsion between the electrons in the beam is required for design work on beam deflection and focusing.

Models of Electrical Conduction

The intuitive model of atomic structure suitable for this elementary stage is of a sphere from which electrons, usually only one, can be removed, leaving a positively charged ion. This process needs a specific quantity of energy called the **ionization energy** and results in the formation of an ion-pair, the ion and its electron.

Conduction in gases

We use a gas model of ionizable spherical particles separated by a distance much greater than their diameter and moving at random, at an average speed that increases with temperature.

At room temperature, hardly any particles collide with sufficient energy to cause ionization. Electrons and ions are produced by cosmic rays and terrestrial radioactivity, however, so cool gases do conduct to a minute degree. A dynamic equilibrium exists with the number of ion-pairs being made balanced by the number recombining when an ion and an electron meet during their random motion.

The small conduction in a gas at room temperature can be enhanced by:

    (a) exposure to hot objects: more ions are generated by the absorption of visible and ultra violet radiation and, if the gas becomes hot enough, ionization by collisions can occur appreciably;

    (b) ionizing radiation, as its name suggests, adds to the effect of ambient radiation (cosmic and from radioactivity);

    (c) a strong electric field, that is a large voltage across a small gap, can cause avalanche ionization, using any ions already present. This will be considered after electric fields have been studied.

Conduction in liquids

There are three main classes of liquid conduction:

    (a) Liquid metals, using the same technique as solid metals, which are described shortly.

    (b) Insulators, which are similar to gases. Little conduction takes place until the electric field is strong enough to cause avalanche breakdown.

Forget for the moment energy levels within atoms, wave mechanics and any other more sophisticated ideas you may have met; a simple model is adequate at this point.

The root mean square average would be used, of course.

The resistivity tends to be higher, as in general the atoms in a liquid are further apart than in a solid. The absence of structural regularity has an effect also.

12

(c) Electrolytes; in this case, the ions are already there, free to move under the influence of any applied electric field. Chemical changes take place when they arrive at the electrodes producing the field, and this forms the basis of the electroplating process.

Electrolytes show various types of conducting particle in action. Copper sulphate conducts only by + ions whereas acidified water uses both + and − ions at the same time.

Conduction in solids

Two main classes of solid conduction occur, corresponding to cases (a) and (b) of liquid conduction:

(a) Metals. A useful intuitive model of a metal is a regular structure (lattice) of positive ions, taking up a pattern corresponding to the crystal structure and given overall neutrality by electrons. There is assumed to be one electron per atom on average, but electrons are free to move through the material between impacts that occur between each other and with the lattice ions.

The situation is very like the molecules in a gas undergoing flow, and the term 'electron gas' is sometimes used.

At ordinary temperatures, the electrons have considerable random kinetic energy, which in fact defines the temperature of the metal and explains why metals are good conductors of heat as well as electricity. The effect of a voltage applied across a metal is to add a small drift component to large random velocities.

At elevated temperatures, the random activity will increase and so the voltage difference required to produce a given drift will be greater. In other words, a metal has a positive temperature coefficient of resistivity.

Think of finding your way through a crowd of people; the faster they are moving, the more difficult it is! The general expression for the temperature coefficient α of any quantity X is $X = X_0 (1 + \alpha T)$ where X_0 is the value of X at 0°C and T is in °C.

(b) Non-metals (insulators and semi-conductors). As with metals, the structure is assumed to be a regular lattice, but this time usually of atoms. At absolute zero, all the atoms are complete and there are no free electrons. To liberate an electron so it can move freely requires a quantity of energy termed the **gap energy**, E_g. If the temperature of the material is raised from absolute zero, then because of the more vigorous random motion of the atoms, an increasing fraction of them will collide with an energy greater than E_g, releasing an electron. Conduction will increase with temperature in this case, so a non-metal has a negative temperature coefficient of resistivity.

A work function also exists for both metals and non-metals, but this is to remove an electron completely. Its importance is mentioned under thermionic emission in Chapter 10.

The conduction process itself is more complex than in metals, for it takes place using not only the electrons freed as just described. When these electrons are released, they each leave behind a positively charged ion. An electron in a neighbouring atom may jump 'into' this ion, leaving behind a new ion in its turn and this process can continue indefinitely. A region of positive charge, associated with each ion in turn, moves through the material just like a positively charged particle would, and is termed a 'hole'. Conduction in insulators and semi-conductors is by both electrons and holes, therefore, not by electrons alone.

In semiconductors the proportion of conduction taking place by either holes or electrons can be changed by doping. See Ritchie, Chapter 1.

Insulators can also undergo avalanche breakdown.

Resistive Circuit Components

Practical resistors

When introducing resistance into a circuit, two points need to be appreciated:

Note the use of word endings in these and similar cases:

-or : a component;
-ance : property of a component;
-ivity : property of a material.

This is discussed in Chapters 4 and 8.

(a) A component purchased as a 'resistor' will have in addition the properties of capacitance and self-inductance. Generally these are only important when high frequency signals are being used, for reasons that will become clear in later sections.

(b) The resistance of an individual component will be within a quoted percentage of that value only when first purchased and while used where it will not heat up to any extent.

For more detail see Loveday, Chapter 3.

The major technologies for producing resistors will now be described briefly and examples of manufacturers' data given. There is no space to discuss the structure of variable resistors, but the resistive elements used in them have the same properties as those dealt with below.

Composition resistors

A mixture of powdered carbon, filler and binder is compressed into a rod and fired. Connecting wires are attached to the ends and the component is either lacquered or dipped in plastic as a hermetic seal.

Film resistors

See also Fig. 2.9. In some cases ('thick film') the substrate is a flat block rather than a rod.

An insulating rod of, for example, alumina is coated with a conducting film and a spiral groove cut in the film. The current path is a helix, therefore, and its resistance is controlled by the pitch of the helix; more 'turns per mm' means both a longer and a narrower strip of film is used and thus a higher resistance is produced, as discussed in Problem 2.1.

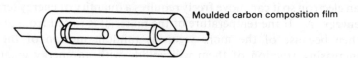

Moulded carbon composition film

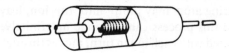

Moulded wirewound

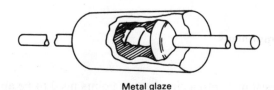

Metal glaze

Fig. 2.5   Examples of fixed resistors (courtesy VTM(UK)Ltd,Greenford,Middx).

Wire-wound resistors

These are used either for high-precision or for high power.

A high-resistance alloy wire, often with near-zero temperature coefficient, is wound on a ceramic rod and coated with enamel.

When used, two important points need to be remembered:

(a) The heat generated must be allowed to escape, so adequate ventilation must be provided;

(b) such a resistor is also a coil and may have considerable self-inductance, as discussed in Chapter 8. This can cause a problem even at high audio frequencies, that is from a few kilohertz, but can reduced by winding half the resistor in the opposite sense to the rest.

The structure of a few types is given in Fig. 2.5.

Resistive transducers

Any component whose resistance changes with some alteration in its environment can be used as a transducer to measure that alteration.

Metal resistance thermometers

The temperature coefficient of resistivity is for pure metals accurately known and relatively large, around 0.3% per °C, but is reduced dramatically by alloying. Pure metals are used invariably for resistance thermometers, therefore. Platinum is, though expensive, a popular choice as it does not corrode. Figure 2.6 shows a commercial platinum film element.

Expansion changes the resistance also, but only by around 10^{-3}% per °C, so is a second-order effect.

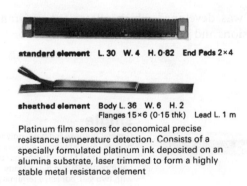

standard element   L. 30   W. 4   H. 0·82   End Pads 2×4

sheathed element   Body L. 36   W. 6   H. 2
Flanges 15×6 (0·15 thk)   Lead L. 1 m

Platinum film sensors for economical precise resistance temperature detection. Consists of a specially formulated platinum ink deposited on an alumina substrate, laser trimmed to form a highly stable metal resistance element

Fig. 2.6   Platinum film detector (courtesy RS Components Ltd, Corby, Northants).

Thermistors

Semiconductors behave in a similar way to insulators, as explained above, and their resistivity decreases with temperature, with a substantially greater negative coefficient than the positive one of even a pure metal. The coefficient itself is not constant with temperature as in a metal, but obeys an inverse square law, resulting in a highly non-linear resistance/temperature graph as Fig. 2.7 shows. Thermistors, which use such materials, are used where small temperature changes need to be measured with simple circuitry but not to a very high accuracy. They are

Moreover, platinum resistance is one of the standard temperature scales, so temperatures measured will always be exactly right on this scale, with known corrections to fit the absolute (thermodynamic) scale.

miniature bead type

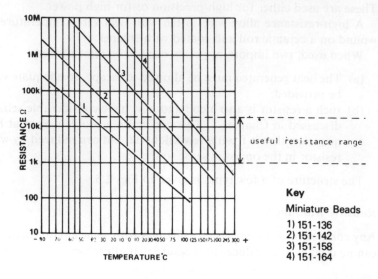

Miniature glass-encapsulated thermistors for temperature measurement and control applications. Selection tolerance ± 20% at 20 °C. Recommended temperature range gives a bead resistance variation from 20 kΩ to 1 kΩ.

Res. at 25 °C	temp. range	equivalent to	stock no.
1 kΩ	{ −40 +25 °C	GM102 VA3400	**151–136**
4·7 kΩ	{ −5 +70 °C	GM472 VA3404	**151–142**
47 kΩ	{ +50 +150 °C	GM473 VA3410	**151–158**
470 kΩ	{ +110 +240 °C	GM474	**151–164**

Graphs of resistance Vs temperature at zero power

Key
Miniature Beads
1) 151-136
2) 151-142
3) 151-158
4) 151-164

Fig. 2.7   Some thermistor data (courtesy RS Components Ltd).

These lines are straight only because they are plotted logarithmically. Try plotting a few points to linear scales to see the non-linearity.

also ideal for temperature-control systems where their large coefficient is more important than good linearity. Some manufacturer's data is given in Fig. 2.7.

Strain gauges

Earlier, Eqn (2.11) was developed which relates the resistance of a block of material to its dimensions and its resistivity. Substituting R for V/I in this equation gives:

$$R = \rho l/A \tag{2.19}$$

L. 13
W. 4

Backing material colour coded: **Type 11** – Red, **Type 23** – Blue.

$$\text{gauge factor} = \frac{\text{fractional resistance increase}}{\text{strain}}$$

single

General purpose foil type, polyester backed strain gauges. Available with temperature compensation for steel (**type 11**) or aluminium (**type 23**). Each gauge has integral 30 mm flying leads. Supplied complete with two self-adhesive terminal pads to facilitate connection to the gauge, without risk of damage by applying undue heat or mechanical stress whilst connecting sensing leads to the device.

technical specification

Gauge length 8 mm
Measurable strain 3 to 4% max.
Temperature range −30 °C to +80 °C
Gauge resistance 120 Ω ±0·5%
Gauge factor 2·1 ±1% (temp. coeff. <5%/100 °C)
Fatigue life >10⁶ reversals at 1000 μ Strain
Foil material copper-nickel alloy
Base material Polyester
Compensation Type 11 Mild steel. Linear
        Expansion factor 10·8×10⁻⁶/°C
        Type 23 Aluminium. Linear
        Expansion factor 23·4×10⁻⁶/°C

Fig. 2.8   Metal strain gauge data (courtesy RS Components Ltd).

When a block of material is deformed, the change in shape will alter its resistance; the block can be used as a strain gauge, therefore, whose task is to measure small changes in the dimensions of the surface to which it has been fixed.

Moreover, the resistivity of many materials alters when they are deformed, providing an additional change in resistance. This piezo-resistive effect is very marked for some semiconductors, though it is not such a linear variation as it is for metals. Figure 2.8 gives some data on a commercially available metal gauge.

The resistance of the gauge will have a temperature coefficient also, so any application will need to compensate for this, perhaps by using an unstrained gauge in a bridge circuit. See Problem 2.4.

Summary

Electric current I is a flow of electric charge Q given by:

$$I = dQ/dt \quad \text{and} \quad Q = \int I dt.$$

Current $I = nAqv$ where I flows in a rod of cross-sectional area A and is made up of n carriers per metre^3, each of charge q and travelling at an average velocity v.

The e.m.f. of a voltage source is the energy given to 1 C of charge flowing through the source at a sufficiently slow rate to lose negligible energy within the source itself; e.m.f. = open-circuit voltage.

For a component, resistance $R = V/I$ where V is the voltage difference between its terminals. For most components R is independent of V at constant temperature (Ohm's law). Conductance $G = I/V$.

For a rod of length l and cross-sectional area A, $R = \rho l/A = l/\sigma A$ for current flowing along the rod length, where ρ is the resistivity and σ the conductivity of the rod material.

Current flux is the total current crossing a given area; current flux density J at a point is defined such that

$$I = \iint J.dA; \quad \oiint J.dA = 0 \text{ for steady currents and } = -dQ/dt.$$

while charge is flowing temporarily.

Conduction in gases occurs when ions are created by heat, radiation or the avalanche effect when existing ions accelerate.

Conduction in liquids is either by metallic conduction, avalanche breakdown or electrolytic processes.

Conduction in solids is either by metallic conduction using one electron per atom (good, with positive temperature coefficient of resistivity) or non-metallic using available ions (poor, with negative temperature coefficient). Semiconductors behave like insulators generally.

Most resistors are made of film, carbon powder or metal wire.

Temperature can be measured by a metal resistance thermometer or thermistor by using its temperature coefficient, that of the former being smaller but more accurately defined than the latter.

If solids are deformed, their resistance changes and this can be used in making strain gauges.

Problems

*Indicates more challenging parts of problems.

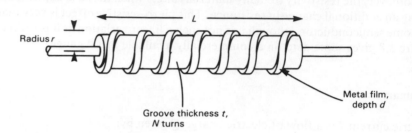

Fig. 2.9   Metal film resistor for Problem 2.1.

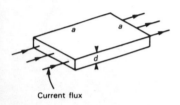

Current flux

If you wish, try it without making these assumptions, but be warned — you get a quartic! Alternatively, put your answer to (c) into the equation from (b) and see how close the resistance is to 150 kΩ.

2.1   (a) Show that if a square slab of material is considered, and current flows as parallel flux lines between two edges as in the diagram in the margin, then its resistance is always given by ρ/d, regardless of dimension a.

*(b) This part applies the concept of 'resistance per square' developed in (a) to a metal film rod resistor as shown in Fig. 2.9.
Assuming N is large enough that effects at the ends of the spiral track are negligible, show that the effective number of 'squares' in the track is given by

$$\frac{N\sqrt{(4\pi^2 r^2 N^2 + L^2)}}{L - Nt}$$

(c) Use the equation from (b) to find the number of turns N required to make a 150 kΩ resistor using a nichrome film of depth 0.02 μm. Use a rod of length 8 mm and diameter 2 mm and assume that L^2 is negligible compared with $4\pi^2 r^2 N^2$. (Resistivity of nichrome is $10^{-6}\Omega$m.)

2.2   Figure 2.10 shows a simple temperature measurement circuit using a thermistor represented by line 2 in Fig 2.7.
By taking spot readings from the characteristic, plot a calibration curve so that the meter, which has a 0 - 100 μA scale, can be used to indicate temperature. Measure the distances carefully, and remember the characteristics are logarithmic.

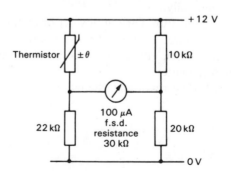

Fig. 2.10   Measurement circuit for Problem 2.2.

18

2.3 The manufacturer of the thermistors whose temperature/resistance characteristics are shown in Fig. 2.7 states that the temperature coefficient α of a thermistor can be described by the equation:

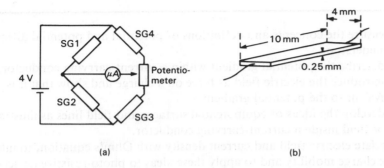

(a)   (b)

Fig. 2.11   Bridge circuit and strain gauge for Problem 2.4.

$$\alpha = -B/T^2$$
or by $\quad R_2 = R_1 \exp[B(1/t_2 - 1/t_1)]$

where B is a constant for a particular type of thermistor, T is in K, R_1 is the resistance at temperature t_1 and R_2 at t_2.

*(a) Show that the two equations are consistent.

(b) Determine B for some of the thermistors given in Fig. 2.7.

2.4 Figure 2.11 (a) shows a bridge circuit for use with semiconductor strain gauges whose structure is given in Fig. 2.11 (b). Other data is provided below.

(a) Estimate the unstrained resistance at 300 K of each gauge.

(b) If SG1 and SG3 are unstrained (for temperature compensation) and the bridge is first balanced, calculate the reading on the microammeter when a strain of 0.01% is applied to SG2 and SG4 (in the same direction for each) and determine which side of the meter would be positive. You may regard the meter current as much smaller than that through the gauges, and disregard the potentiometer resistance also.

Data: gauge factor (see Fig. 2.8)   : -130
      unstrained resistivity   : 0.1 Ω m at 300 K
      microammeter resistance   : 500 Ω

3 Potential and the Electric Field

Objectives

☐ To ensure the concepts and definitions of potential and potential difference are understood.

☐ To describe the potential gradient within a current-carrying conductor.

☐ To introduce the electric field as force on a charge and show that it is equivalent to the potential gradient.

☐ To develop the ideas of equipotential surfaces and field lines as illustrations of the field inside a current-carrying conductor.

☐ To relate electric field and current density with Ohm's equation, to introduce charge mobility and to apply these ideas to photo-resistive devices.

☐ To extend the ideas of potential gradient and electric field from within a conductor into the space between conductors and to introduce the line integral.

☐ To show how equipotential surfaces lead to the concept of a conservative field and how this can be described using a loop integral.

☐ To show how electric fields can accelerate charged particles, and to apply this to gas-discharge tubes.

Potential (Voltage) in a Circuit

An intuitive model of an earth is described shortly.

If a voltmeter, regarded for the moment as a 'black box', is connected across a battery, the reading can be interpreted in several ways. It is always the 'battery voltage' or, better, the 'potential difference across the battery', but if one of the battery terminals is called '0 volts' or 'earth', this fixes the potentials of the whole circuit, as indicated in Fig. 3.1.

If the battery drives current through a wire, the voltmeter can be connected across different parts of the wire to show the change in potential experienced by charge moving round the circuit.

Remembering the connection between voltage and energy in Eqn (2.7), it is now possible to define potential difference and potential.

Potentials
3 2 1 0

Uniform resistance wire

1 V reading

If point *B* were called +6 V, *A* would be at a potential of +9 V, and so on.

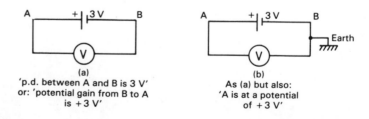

(a)
'p.d. between A and B is 3 V'
or: 'potential gain from B to A is +3 V'

(b)
As (a) but also:
'A is at a potential of +3 V'

Fig. 3.1   Potential and potential difference.

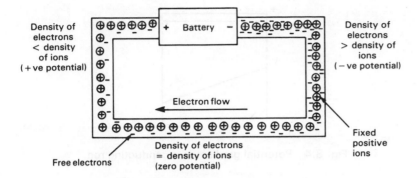

Density of
electrons
< density
of ions
(+ ve potential)

Density of
electrons
> density of
ions
(− ve potential)

Electron flow

Free electrons

Density of electrons
= density of ions
(zero potential)

Fixed
positive
ions

Fig. 3.2   An intuitive model of a d.c. circuit.

The **potential difference** (p.d.) between two points is the energy change involved when unit charge is transferred by any path between them. The p.d. between a point and an earth is called simply the **potential** at that point.

An intuitive model of potential in a circuit can be made along the following lines. In uncharged metal, electrons are free to move among fixed positive charges and, ignoring random motion, will be evenly distributed because of mutual repulsion. The positive terminal of a battery will remove electrons from that part of the circuit connected to it, and the negative terminal will repel them into the other end of the circuit, as Fig. 3.2 shows.

This diagram would fit an isolated circuit, where halfway round could be considered as zero potential and the battery terminals equally positive and negative. If the negative battery terminal were earthed, electrons would be removed until the distribution was even there, so the positive terminal would be 'doubly plus' compared with the isolated case; the difference between positive and negative would still be the same, of course.

Potential gradient

To understand the concept of potential under conditions when no current flows, electrostatic conditions, you need to appreciate first the way potential can be distributed both within and outside a current-carrying conductor. At the same time, to describe in a useful way how currents flow we need to look at a point within a circuit, and ask what an electron at that point actually experiences.

Consider Fig. 3.3(a), which is a circuit of two batteries, low-resistance wires and a rod of material, whose resistance is much greater than that of the rest of the circuit.

In practice, one coulomb would make an enormous difference, but the principle applies. If this worries you, think of transferring a picocoulomb (10^{-12} C), measuring the energy then multiplying by 10^{12}. The significance of 'by any path' will be explained later, when the conservative field concept is explained.

This uses the fixed +, moving − model for a metal from Chapter 2.

Assuming the local earth actually does correspond to an equal density of electrons and + charges; you cannot tell locally whether this is so or not.

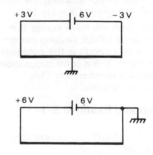

Of course, if the wires to the rod mid-point were merged, zero net current would flow as it is equal and opposite in Fig. 3.3(b). The wires could therefore be removed without effect, re-creating Fig. 3.3(a).

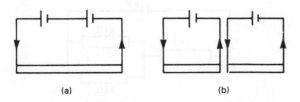

(a)   (b)

Fig. 3.3   Potential halfway down a conducting rod.

21

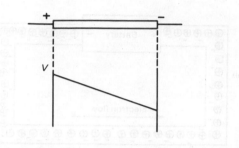

Fig. 3.4 Potential gradient in a conducting rod.

If you think this is obvious, it is because superposition has become so deeply ingrained in you!

In practice, of course, a voltmeter would be used, connected between one end of the rod and other points to plot the graph, but this can only be justified if the voltmeter is thought of as a 'battery counter'.

Note that the zero of potential has not been marked, for the reasons explained above; only the shape of the graph concerns us here.

This looks like the answer to the instantaneous switching problem in Chapter 2, but it's not the whole story; it takes time for the potential gradient to take effect all along the rod — more in Chapter 11.

Although we have stated that the local effect causing current flow in a circuit is the potential gradient, there is no suggestion yet of a mechanism. This follows shortly.

Worked Example 3.1

Yorke, chapter 1, covers this type of problem.

If the rod is uniform, the current flow will be parallel, so the current density will be constant at all points. Because of superposition we could produce the same current by driving each half of the rod from separate batteries as Fig. 3.3(b) shows. Thus halfway down the rod the potential itself is halfway between the potentials at the two ends. Similarly, one quarter of the way down it would be one quarter of the total p.d.

By extending this argument at tedious length, we could justify the statement that the potential at each point in the rod depends linearly on its distance from one end. A graph could be drawn of potential against position, and would obviously look like Fig. 3.4.

In the intuitive model developed at the beginning of the chapter, the electron density would increase at a steady rate as one moved from the more positive to the more negative part of the rod.

If the e.m.f. is increased, by using more batteries in series, a greater current flows in the rod (proportional to the e.m.f. if the circuit is ohmic). Although this is obvious for the whole circuit, it is less clear when only a tiny part of the rod is considered: how does it 'know' that the p.d. between the ends of the rods is bigger? The answer comes from the graph in Fig. 3.4. If the battery e.m.f. is bigger, the graph will be steeper, and this will apply to all points in the rod, not just to the ends. So the electrical behaviour at any point in the rod depends on the gradient of the graph at that point, the **potential gradient**, measured in volt metre^{-1}.

Calculate the potential gradient within the 1 kΩ resistor in the circuit Fig. 3.5, if the resistive material is of length 5 mm.

Solution: We need to find the potential difference between the ends of the resistor, by the usual circuit theory calculations, then divide it by the length of the resistive material.

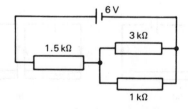

Fig. 3.5 Circuit for Worked Example 3.1.

Working in kilohms:
Equivalent resistance R of the 3 kΩ and 1 kΩ resistors in parallel is given by:

$$1/R = 1/3 + 1/1 = 4/3$$
so
$$R = 3/4 \text{ kΩ}$$

Using the potential divider rule (p.d. across resistors in a series circuit $\propto$ resistance):

$$\frac{\text{p.d. across 1 kΩ resistor}}{\text{p.d. across whole chain}} = 0.75/2.25 = 1/3$$

thus p.d. across resistor = $6 \times 1/3 = 2$ V
so potential gradient = $2/(5 \times 10^{-3}) = 400$ V/m

Electric Field

In the rod discussed above, we decided that the local effect of all the potentials and resistances in the circuit was the potential gradient at the point being considered.

It may be wondered why we need to bring in a new idea, potential gradient, as the cause of current flow. We could explain it simply on the basis of charges attracting and repelling: electrons in the rod are repelled by the negative battery terminal and attracted by the positive.

Although this simple idea is adequate for a first look, calculations cannot easily be based on it. How can the actual charge at the battery terminals be determined? What effect do all the other charges in the rod have?

We need to consider the local effect from the point of view of an electron; what is actually there, where the electron is, which causes it to move? The electron must feel a force, to make it move, and the term **electric field at a point** has been invented to describe this.

By analogy with gravitational field, which is the force acting on one unit of mass, 1 kg, electric field can be defined as the force acting on one unit of electric charge, that is 1 coulomb. So the force F acting on Q coulombs due to an electric field of strength E can be expressed by:

$$\mathbf{F} = Q\mathbf{E} \tag{3.1}$$

This gives the units of E as newton coulomb^{-1}. The bold type shows that the direction of both F and E is as important as their magnitude. In other words F and E are vectors and in this equation act in the same direction; the direction of an electric field at any point is the direction a positive charge placed there will move under its influence.

We are now in a somewhat unsatisfactory position, with two different ideas expressing the local effect causing current to flow in a circuit:

(a) The **potential gradient**, measured in V m^{-1} and expressing the rate at which potential changes with distance at points observed in succession round a circuit. The larger this is at a particular point, the larger will be the current there in a simple parallel-flow case.

(b) The **electric field**, measured in N C^{-1} and based on the force acting on an electric charge such as an electron at a point in a circuit.

A negative charge, like an electron, will move in the opposite direction to the quoted direction of E. In the equation this is expressed by a negative value of Q. If this worries you, think of objects in a tank of water in a gravitational field; a stone sinks, following gravitational field lines, whereas a ping-pong ball rises, moving 'against' them!

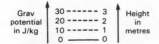

Force on 1 kg near the earth's surface is 10 N, so gravitational potential energy increases by 10 J for each metre 1 kg is raised.

This itself follows from energy transfer (work) = force × distance. See any basic mechanics or Physics book. The potential energy need not be gravitational; it could, for example, be elastic or, as we shall see, electrical.

This is an incomplete equation, where V is changing only in the x direction. If it changes in other directions also, the voltage gradient components need to be added as vectors (they can be by superposition). The vector addition produces a quantity called grad V, as described in Carter, chapter 1. Eqn(3.4) is equal to grad V for changes in the x direction only.

The units show the equivalence nicely: V/m = J/Cm = Nm/Cm = N/C.

Ignoring random motion imposed by thermal agitation, of course.

Even in a complicated field, if a small enough region is inspected then for all practical purposes the field lines will be parallel and equipotential surfaces plane.

This is exactly like situations in mechanics where an object falls due to gravity. Its motion can be described either in terms of the action of a gravitational force or by using the idea of gravitational potential energy. On the moon, we can say that the gravitational potential energy gradient is less than it is on the earth, so objects fall with a lower acceleration, gaining kinetic energy more slowly.

The equation connecting force F with gravitational potential energy gradient $\mathrm{d}W/\mathrm{d}x$ is:

$$F = -\mathbf{d}W/\mathbf{d}x \qquad (3.2)$$

The minus sign represents the fact that gravitational potential energy increases as you go up, so its gradient is in an upward direction, whereas the gravitational force on an object is downwards. Note that $\mathbf{d}W/\mathbf{d}x$ is a vector quantity, having a direction along x in the direction of W increasing, even though W itself is scalar, having size or magnitude only.

We can write an exactly equivalent equation for the force on and energy of a constant electric charge in an electric field.

$F = -\mathbf{d}W/\mathbf{d}x$ [Eqn (3.2)] while $F = QE$ [Eqn (3.1)] and $W = QV$ [Eqn (2.7)]. So:

$$QE = -Q\mathbf{d}V/\mathbf{d}x \qquad (3.3)$$
$$\text{thus} \quad E = -\mathbf{d}V/\mathbf{d}x \qquad (3.4)$$

So the electric field at a point, defined as force per coulomb, is of equal size and of opposite direction to the potential gradient at that point. Usually potential gradient is easier to measure or predict than electric field, as the latter requires force on a charge to be measured. Not only is this rarely easy, but the presence of the test charge would alter the charge distribution setting up the field in the first place. Potential or voltage measurements can be carried out easily and, by using potentiometric methods, need cause little disturbance to the field.

However, neither one of these two concepts should be regarded as more fundamental than the other; they are two sides of the same coin. Which one is used in any particular case depends entirely on convenience or ease of calculation, in the same way as one chooses to use either force or potential energy change in mechanics.

We can now turn our attention to what happens in space, where there are no charges to move. To prepare the way, we need first to look at how potentials and fields can be represented on diagrams.

Equipotential surfaces and field lines

Figure 3.6 shows part of the conducting rod discussed earlier, with the two essential parts of its geometry marked. *a* and *b* are cross-sections of the rod, circular planes at right angles to the rod axis, and *c* is one of an infinite set of lines in the rod and parallel to its axis.

In terms of the concepts met already, *c* is the direction in which charge would flow to make up a current in the rod, and thus can be described as a **field line**. The direction of E will always be along a line like *c*, and no component of current flow at right angles to *c* will occur.

The potential changes at a uniform rate moving down the rod, but cannot change in a direction at right angles to the rod axis; if it did then current would flow at right angles, and we have just said that it does not! Thus the potential within planes like *a* and *b* will be the same at all points.

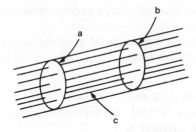

Fig. 3.6 Lines and surfaces within a rod.

Although in this case *a* and *b* are planes, in more complex cases they may be curved in various ways, so they are referred to as **Equipotential surfaces**.

From these arguments it should be clear that electric field lines, or *E* lines, are always at right angles, that is normal to equipotential surfaces.

If equipotential surfaces are drawn at equal changes of potential, the pattern of a field can be seen, which may if desired be clarified further by drawing in the field lines normal to these surfaces. This will be pursued further when fields in space are discussed, but a simple conduction example will be given, for the case where a thick wire joins on to a thinner one. See Fig. 3.7, which shows a potential plot as well.

Because of local effects binding the electrons into the metal, they are constrained to run parallel to the surface when at the surface. Equipotential surfaces within a current-carrying conductor therefore meet the surface at right angles. As the wire thins, making its resistance per unit length increase, two effects can be seen:

(a) The density or closeness of field lines increases as we move into the thinner

In the marginal figure near Eqn(3.2), the horizontal lines represent gravitational equipotential surfaces. These are spherical shells if the earth's curvature is taken into account. Gravitational field lines are vertical, by definition!

Equipotential surfaces need not be equally spaced in potential, but often are. Carter, chapter 3, shows how problems with more complex geometries can be solved.

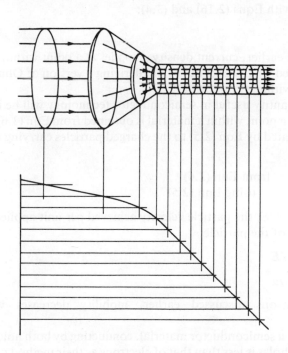

Fig. 3.7 Field lines and equipotential surfaces.

wire, as the paths of moving charge cannot appear or disappear within the conductor.

(b) To represent the increased potential gradient as we move into a zone of higher resistance per unit length, the equipotential surfaces must get closer together.

As we already know that field and potential gradient are the same thing really, this suggests that the density of field lines represents the strength of the fields. We shall return to this idea in Chapter 4.

Conduction and Charge Mobility

In this section we connect together Ohm's equation and the electric field causing electrons to move within a conductor.

As before, we consider a rod carrying a uniform flux of current, but so we can extend the idea to a point within any conductor, the rod will be shrunk to infinitesimal size. The rod is of length dx, area of cross-section dA and carries a current dI, for which a potential difference of dV is required across it.

First we shall transform Ohm's equation into a form that applies at a point rather than over the volume of an electrical component.

$$I = VA\sigma/l \qquad \text{[from Eqn (2.12)]}$$

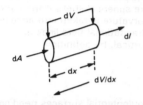

dA direction of *I*, **dx** in direction of *V* increasing.

Replacing the quantities with those in the marginal figure above, and noting the directions of dA and dx:

$$dI/dA = -\sigma dV/dx \tag{3.5}$$

Combining with Eqns (2.16) and (3.4):

$$J = \sigma E \tag{3.6}$$

As explained earlier, current density J applies at a point within a conductor, so we have achieved what we set out to do, deriving a version of Ohm's equation for use at a point within a conductor.

Finally, a quantity useful in semiconductor technology will be introduced. The conductivity at a point within a material is obtained from Eqn (3.6) immediately. J itself can be related by Eqn (2.5) to the charged particles carrying the current, and thus:

$$\sigma = J/E \qquad \text{from Eqn (3.6)}$$
$$= nqv/E \qquad \text{using Eqn (2.5)}$$

The quantity v/E, the particle velocity achieved per unit applied field, is called the **mobility**, μ of the particle:

$$\mu = v/E \tag{3.7}$$

Thus $\qquad \sigma = nq\mu \tag{3.8}$

Mobility is constant for most materials at low fields, but decreases at high values:

See, for example, Solymar and Walsh, chapter 8.

For the reasons discussed earlier, mobility decreases with increasing temperature.

In the case of a semiconductor material, conducting by both holes and electrons, the mobility of holes is less than that of electrons as their method of propagation is more complicated. The contributions of both holes and electrons must be added to calculate the conductivity.

Worked Example 3.2

(a) Calculate the resistance between the flat faces of a cylindrical bead of pure silicon (1 mm dia × 1 mm) at 300 K and 400 K, using the data for silicon given:

	300 K	400 K
Carrier concentration (either type) n_i	7×10^{15}	2.6×10^{18} m^{-3}
Electron mobility	0.135	0.09 m^{2}V^{-1} s^{-1}
Hole mobility	0.048	0.03 m^2 V^{-1} s^{-1}

The charge on the electron is 1.6×10^{-19}.

(b) Using the same data as in part (a), calculate the drift speed of electrons and holes at 300 K when a voltage of 10 V is applied across the flat faces of the bead.

Solution:

(a) Clearly, Eqn (2.12) and Eqn (3.8) will be required, using the values of n and μ given.

As each carrier contributes to the conductivity σ, then using Eqn (3.8):

$$\sigma = (nq\mu)_{\text{electrons}} + (nq\mu)_{\text{holes}}$$

In this case, n and q are the same for each, so:

At 300 K: $\sigma = 1.6 \times 10^{-19} \times 7 \times 10^{15} (0.135 + 0.048) = 2.05 \times 10^{-4}$ S m^{-1}

At 400 K: $\sigma = 1.6 \times 10^{-19} \times 2.6 \times 10^{18} (0.09 + 0.03) = 5.00 \times 10^{-2}$ S m^{-1}

Note how the increase in carrier population overwhelms the decrease in mobility as the temperature rises.

From these, using Eqn (2.12):

Resistance = $l/\sigma A$ = 6.2 MΩ at 300 K
= 25.5 kΩ at 400 K

(b) Resist the temptation to use the answer to part (a) and equation Eqn (2.6), or any other method that involves calculating current. The concept of mobility allows an immediate calculation, using Eqn (3.7):

Rearranging Eqn (3.7): $v = \mu E$
for electrons = $0.135 \times 10/10^{-3} = 1350$ m s^{-1}
for holes = $0.048 \times 10/10^{-3} = 480$ m s^{-1}

Compare these with the answer to Worked Example 2.1.

Control of particle mobility is an important factor in tailoring semiconductor materials for particular applications. A very high mobility is required, for instance, in materials used for infra-red and visible light detectors and for Hall effect devices.

These are discussed later in this chapter, and in Chapter 10, respectively.

Light-dependent resistors

In Chapter 2, conduction in an insulator or semiconductor was described in terms of an energy gap E_g, a minimum quantity of energy that atoms must receive in order to become an electron-hole pair. Light energy can be shown to arrive at an illuminated surface in 'packets' called quanta, whose energy content depends on the light's frequency or colour. If the quanta are of energy greater than E_g for a material, electron-hole pairs will be generated and it will conduct when illuminated.

However, a piece of such a material will only make a useful light detector if the charge carriers can make their way to its edge without combining with another carrier of the opposite sign.

The lower the carrier concentration and the shorter is the path to be followed, the greater is their probability of doing this, and the higher will be the detection efficiency of the device.

However, a short path length must be combined with a large width, otherwise the area exposed to light will be small, and the device insensitive. Also, low carrier concentration must if possible be combined with a high mobility otherwise, from Eqn (3.8), the device resistance will be uncomfortably high.

The energy gap for a suitable material must be less than the quantum energy of the light to be detected. However, if it is too low, thermal energy will itself cause conduction and make the device conduct even in the absence of light.

For far infrared work, using low energy gap materials, devices have to be cooled to very low temperatures to reduce carrier generation by thermal processes.

All this leads to a device in which a narrow strip of light-sensitive material is made up into a two-terminal device behind a transparent window. The material has an E_g just low enough to detect the reddest light required, a low n and a high μ. Cadmium sulphide (CdS) is used for visible light, though its mobility is rather low. For infrared detectors, indium antimonide (InSb), with a very high mobility and small E_g, comes into its own.

Figure 3.8 shows an ORP12 light dependent resistor, in which the strip of CdS exposed to light is zig-zagged to give as large a width as possible. Its resistance/illumination curve is also shown.

In a sense, however, we have already been dealing with fields in space. When the force on an electron was under discussion, it was considered in isolation and without reference to the electron's immediate neighbours. In practice the electric forces on a conduction electron are very complex. Luckily, however, because of the structural symmetry of conducting materials, the effects of nearby charges largely cancel out, apart from local changes in electron density caused by the applied potential gradient. These changes cause exactly the same effect on the electron as it would feel were it in isolation and subjected to the same potential gradient.

For a more complete description see for example *Nuffield A-Level Teachers' Guide*: Original version unit 3, Revised version unit E.

Potential and Field in Space

So far our concern has been with events within an electric circuit. This was because most students are more familiar with electric circuits than with electrostatic situations.

However, we now move into the realm of genuine electrostatics. As its name suggests, the laws of electrostatics apply when no charges move. Conductors are allowed to be present but no currents flow, which immediately ensures a very simple law to begin with:

The surfaces of all conductors in an electrostatic situation are equipotential surfaces; if they were not, currents would flow within them.

Figure 3.9(a) shows a simple experimental arrangement to demonstrate the essential similarities between electric fields in space and those in conducting materials. It consists of a pair of parallel plates connected to a voltage source. By using a flame probe connected to a very high-resistance voltmeter, the potential at various points between and outside the plates can be measured, and thus equipo-

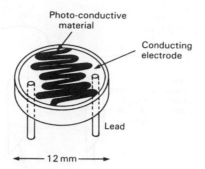

Spectral response

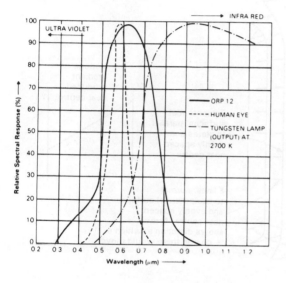

Cell resistance v illumination

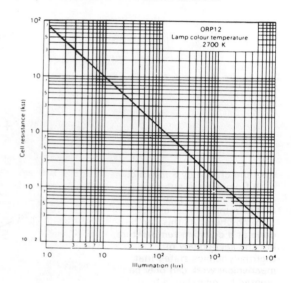

Fig. 3.8   CdS photoresistor type ORP12 (data courtesy RS Components Ltd).

tential surfaces and potential gradients obtained, as illustrated in Fig. 3.9(b).

Much more difficult experiments can be devised in which the force on a known small charge in the space can be measured, to confirm the idea that the situation is exactly the same as in a conductor. All the equations relating to field and voltage gradient are found to apply. The space between the plates has been altered in such a way that if a small charge is placed there, it moves along field lines, at right angles to equipotential surfaces.

The electric field under electrostatic conditions has one very important property, which follows from equipotential surfaces. If equipotential surfaces exist, then each point in the field must have a unique value of potential. Therefore if a path is followed from one point to another in a field, the net change in potential from start to finish does not depend on the actual path taken.

Such a field, for which energy changes are independent of the path followed, is called **conservative field**. Gravitation is another example, but the electric field generated by a changing magnetic field is not so.

Assuming that the presence of the charge does not alter the charges on the plates setting up the field.

This can also be argued thermodynamically as follows. If a + charge is taken from a point to another at a higher potential, work has to be done on it. If the charge is then moved back to its original point, that work can be regained. if the potential change depended on the actual path, we could

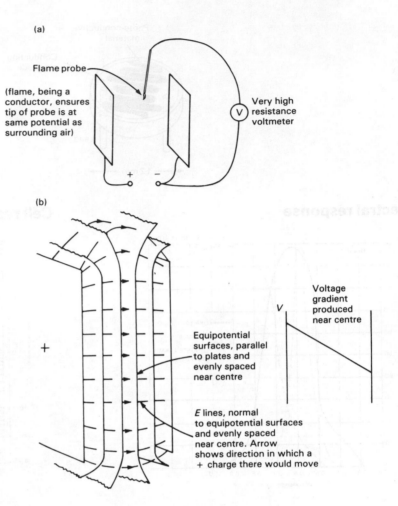

(a)

Flame probe

(flame, being a conductor, ensures tip of probe is at same potential as surrounding air)

V Very high resistance voltmeter

+ −

(b)

+

V Voltage gradient produced near centre

Equipotential surfaces, parallel to plates and evenly spaced near centre

E lines, normal to equipotential surfaces and evenly spaced near centre. Arrow shows direction in which a + charge there would move

Fig. 3.9   Electric field between parallel plates.

take the charge by a low p.d. path from *A* to *B*, but let it return by a higher p.d. path, and gain mechanical energy from nowhere. All this can be done at a constant temperature, but the second law of thermodynamics states that mechanical work can only be created by operating a heat engine between two temperatures. Therefore the p.d. does not depend on the path followed, a unique potential can be given to each point in an electric field, and equipotential surfaces can be drawn.

Up to this point, calculations have been concerned with highly symmetrical cases. Where *E* lines are in the *x* direction, the simple equation:

$$E = -\mathrm{d}V/\mathrm{d}x \qquad \text{same as Eqn (3.4) can be used.}$$

Exercise 3.1

This assumes a parallel-plate gap. The gap can be smaller if the conductors have a high curvature, as the field lines are concentrated, and the field therefore larger. See earlier references to lightning conductors.

Later chapters and Carter, chapter 1, deal with more sophisticated methods.

Air under normal conditions requires an electric field of 3000 V mm^{-1} for it to break down. Calculate the spark gap needed to prevent the output of a high voltage supply exceeding 100 kV, if parallel plates are used.
(Answer: Gap width = 33 mm.)

In Fig. 3.9(b) can be seen **edge effects**, where the equipotential surfaces are no longer plane. These can be minimized by using plates relatively close together compared with their lengths, but more complex cases will need to be considered at some stage, of course.

Potential difference as a line integral

Up to now, we have been concerned with obtaining a value for E from knowing potential at various points in a field, using Eqn (3.4). There are many examples where the reverse is needed, when E is known over a region and the difference in potential is required between two points in the field. For instance the velocity of a free electron in a cathode ray tube depends on its potential relative to the potential at which its velocity is zero. If it moves in a known field, we may require its velocity at different points.

When E lines are parallel, potential difference $(V_2 - V_1)$ is obtained by merely multiplying field E by distance x moved along the field, taking careful account of direction and, therefore, sign.

When E is varying, but the path along which the potential change is to be calculated is always along an E line, a distance dl must be chosen, infinitesimally small so that E can be regarded as constant, and the infinitesimal increase in potential dV calculated by finding $-Edl$ for that small displacement. The total change is found by adding up all these small products for the motion from l_1 to l_2, in other words by carrying out an integration:

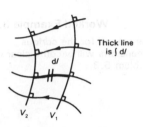

$$\text{change in potential } V_2 - V_1 = -\int_{l_1}^{l_2} Edl \qquad (3.9)$$

Thick line is $\int dl$

Inevitably, situations arise where the path along which the p.d. is to be calculated crosses field lines, as Fig. 3.10 shows. In this case, once again an infinitesimal region has to be considered, so that any local variation in E, either in magnitude or direction, can be ignored.

The local magnitude of E is equal to $-dV/dx$, but the calculation path is along the longer distance dl. However, as the electric field is conservative we can simplify the calculation path AC to a step AB along dx, for which the potential change is simply $-Edx$, followed by a motion BC along the equipotential surface. For this, by definition, there is no potential change so $-Edx$ must be the answer for any path we take from A to C, including the most direct one.

Thus $\qquad dV = -Edx = -Edl\cos\Theta \qquad\qquad (3.10)$

If E and dl are now considered as vectors, the answer can be written as a scalar product of vectors, in a similar way to current flux in Chapter 2:

$$dV = -\mathbf{E}.\mathbf{dl} \qquad (3.11)$$

If the path is along a field line, $\cos\Theta = 1$ and the answer reduces to the simpler one discussed earlier. If on the other hand $\Theta = 90°$, dV becomes zero; not sur-

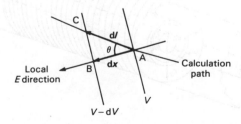

Fig. 3.10   P.d. calculations at an angle to a field line.

prisingly as the motion must then be along a line within an equipotential surface.

To find the potential change for a large movement in a field, the infinitesimal changes dV calculated above need to be added for the whole length of the line. The expression obtained is called a **line integral**:

$$V_2 - V_1 = - \int_{l_1}^{l_2} E.dl \qquad (3.12)$$

This can be compared with Kirchhoff's second law, that voltages around a closed path in a circuit add up to zero.

As compared with $\oint dA$ which is an integral over the whole of an enclosing surface. See Eqn(2.18).

The conservative field property discussed earlier can be neatly summed up in the equation by writing it for the case when the path starts and finishes at the same point. In this case there can be no change in potential, so, for electrostatic fields:

$$\oint E.dl = 0 \qquad (3.13)$$

The symbol $\oint$ is called a loop integral, and implies a path ending where it started.

Worked Example 3.3

The reason for the curious dimensions will become clear in Problem 5.3.

A coaxial cable for high voltage power transmission has a central conductor of diameter 0.0736 m, an outer conductor of diameter 0.2 m and the space between is filled with polythene, of resistivity 10^{13} Ω m. Calculate the leakage current flowing between inner and outer conductor, per kilometre length of cable, when a transmission voltage of 750 kV is used.

Solution: Figure 3.11 shows the arrangement. Current flux lines will be radial, thus closer together nearer the inner conductor; J will be larger there, so will E therefore as Eqn (3.6) shows. We need to use the relation between current and current flux density in the form of Eqn (2.17), combined with the line integral equation Eqn (3.12). E and J can then be eliminated.

At any value of r, the current I leaking through the cylindrical surface of radius r is given by:

$$I = \int J.dA = J \times 2\pi rl \qquad \text{[from Eqn (2.17)]}$$

$$\text{At any point } J = \sigma E \qquad \text{[from Eqn (3.6)]}$$

$$\text{and } V_2 - V_1 = \int E.dl \qquad \text{[from Eqn (3.12)]}$$
$$= \int E dr \qquad \text{as the path is radial}$$

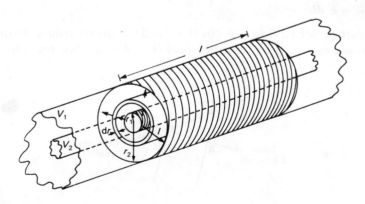

Fig. 3.11 Coaxial conductors for Worked Example 3.3.

Combining these three equations:

$$V_2 - V_1 = \int_{r_1}^{r_2} \frac{I \, dr}{2\pi \, rl\sigma}$$

$$= \left[\frac{I \ln(r)}{2\pi\sigma l} \right]_{r_1}^{r_2}$$

$$= \frac{I \ln(r_2/r_1)}{2\pi\sigma l}$$

so $$I/l = \frac{2\pi \, \sigma(V_2 - V_1)}{\ln(r_2/r_1)}$$

Substituting the numbers from the problem:

$$I/l = 4.7 \times 10^{-7} \text{ A m}^{-1}$$
$$= 0.47 \text{ mA km}^{-1}$$

At 750 kV this represents a loss of over 350 W km^{-1}.

Acceleration of Charged Particles in an Electric Field

In Chapter 10, the motion of charged particles such as electrons in electric and magnetic fields will be discussed in some detail. However, to explain the operation of discharge tubes you need to appreciate the behaviour of such particles in the simple electric field produced by parallel plates.

In the constant electric field E set up in this way, a constant force $F = qE$, from Eqn (3.1), is applied to a particle of charge q. If free to move, it will accelerate at a rate a given from Newton's laws of motion as $a = F/m$ where m is its mass. Thus:

$$\text{acceleration} \quad a = Eq/m \tag{3.14}$$

To find the velocity v achieved by the particle at any point, the acceleration would need to be integrated. As potential is the integral of field anyway, from Eqn (3.12), a simpler process is to use the p.d. between that point and one where the particles are stationary.

If a particle moves through a p.d. ΔV, the actual p.d. is the energy change per unit charge. If the energy change is only from electric field energy to kinetic energy of the particle, which it will be for a free electron for example, then:

$$\Delta V = \frac{mv^2}{2q} \tag{3.15}$$

As $a = dv/dt$, $v_2 - v_1 = \int a \, dt$. However we require an integration w.r.t. distance, for which (energy change $= \int F \, dl$) is a more useful basis. Knowing (or measuring) potentials means that the integration has been carried out already, in effect.

Take Eqn(2.7) and make V the subject.

Note the difference between the response of charges within a conductor, and that of charges as free particles. In a uniform electric field the latter accelerate according to Eqn (3.14), the former travel at a steady speed according to Eqn (2.5) and Eqn (3.6).

Obviously, electrons in a conductor must accelerate up to a uniform speed when a field is applied, but this takes a very short time indeed.

Discharge tubes and fluorescent lights

When gas conduction was examined in Chapter 2, the increased conductivity of a gas when exposed to a large electric field was mentioned. In this section we look in more detail at such gas discharges.

When an electric field is applied to a gas, the few ions that are always present are accelerated according to Eqn (3.14). If no substantial conduction occurs, it means that the kinetic energy of the accelerated ions never reaches the ionization energy of the gas. They are losing sufficient momentum in elastic collisions with uncharged atoms in the gas for this not to happen. However if the combination of electric field strength and mean free path is large enough, the ionization energy can be achieved by some ions, and any atom hit by one of these will itself be ionized.

The ions produced by these inelastic collisions can themselves accelerate and produce more ions; this is called an avalanche process or chain reaction. The whole gas would quickly become a plasma, made up entirely of ions, but for one limitation: the more ions that are present, the more likely it is that a positive ion and a negative ion will meet and recombine. Thus a state of balance, called a dynamic equilibrium, is set up in which as many ions are being formed by collisions as are recombining.

When ions recombine to form an atom once more, the ionization energy is given up again, as light. Thus a gas undergoing discharge will glow. As the ionization energy is different for each gas, the quantum energy of the emitted light will be different and so therefore will be the colour. Display 'strip' lighting is made from tubes of different gases, neon for red, sodium for yellow, and so on.

Domestic white lighting is produced by using mercury vapour, which produces ultra violet light at high efficiency. The inside of the discharge tube is coated with a fluorescent material, which absorbs ultra violet light and gives the energy out as visible white light.

Summary

The p.d. between two points is the energy required to transfer one unit of charge between them. The potential at a point is the energy required to transfer one unit of charge from a defined zero, usually an earth, to the point. A positive potential can be visualized as a region where there is a deficiency of electrons, a negative potential where there is an excess.

The potential gradient at a point is the rate of change of potential with displacement, dV/dx, where dx is measured in the direction of maximum gradient. The electric field E at a point is the force that would act on unit charge at the point. $E = -dV/dx$. A field such as the E field under electrostatic conditions, where the potential at each point is unique, is called a conservative field.

The potential change $V_2 - V_1$ along a path $\int dl$ within a field E is given by $\int E.dl$. If the field is conservative, $\oint E.dl = 0$.

Equipotential Surfaces join points having the same potential. E lines are lines crossing equipotential surfaces at right angles and showing the direction of E at any point. In representations of fields, E lines and equipotential surfaces are both drawn closer together where the field is stronger. The surfaces of all conductors under electrostatic conditions are equipotential.

Current density J and electric field E at a point in a conductor are related by $J = \sigma E$, where σ is the conductivity.

Mobility μ of a charge carrier is defined as the drift velocity attained in unit field. $\sigma = nq\mu$ for carriers of density n and charge q.

Photoresistors work by the generation of electron-hole pairs by light photons.

Suitable materials need a low carrier concentration to reduce recombination and thus a high mobility to keep their resistivity low.

The acceleration a of a charge particle of charge q and mass m in an electric field E is given by $a = Eq/m$.

The speed v gained by a charged particle moving from rest through a potential change ΔV is given by:

$$\Delta V = \frac{mv^2}{2q}$$

Discharge tubes work by accelerating gas ions until they cause further ionization and an avalanche discharge. Light is emitted when the ions recombine.

Problems

*Indicates a more challenging problem.

    Use gravitational field strength $g = 9.8\ \text{N kg}^{-1}\ (\text{m s}^{-2})$

3.1 Calculate the product JE in the following cases. Show also by the units you use that JE could be described as 'power density':

    (a) copper wire ($\sigma = 6 \times 10^7\ \text{S m}^{-1}$) dia 0.6 mm carrying 1 A;

    (b) nichrome wire ($\sigma = 10^6\ \text{S m}^{-1}$) dia 0.4 mm carrying 4 A in a heating element;

    (c) tungsten wire ($\sigma = 2.4 \times 10^5\ \text{S m}^{-1}$ at operating temperature) dia 0.03 mm carrying 0.4 A in a filament light bulb.

> Carter, chapter 3, deals with the concept of power density = $J.E$ in detail.

3.2 Dust particles of mass 5×10^{-12} kg can be given a charge of 2×10^{-10} C in an electrostatic precipitator. What voltage needs to be applied to plates 0.35 m apart in order to apply to the particles a force equal to 100 000 times their own weight?

> Chapter 5 describes the working of practical ones, which charge the dust particles as well as collect them.

3.3 The breakdown electric field for air is of the order of 3000 V mm^{-1}. The most significant ionization energy involved in this breakdown is the lowest, that of oxygen at 12 electron-volts (i.e. $12 \times 1.6 \times 10^{-19}$ joules).

Calculate the acceleration distance required to enable electrons to achieve this energy and cause a discharge. Compare your answer with the mean free path of air particles, which is about 0.2 μm.

*3.4 The potential is measured at 8 points within an electric field. The points are at the corners of a cuboid and are shown in Fig. 3.12.

    (a) Justify the statement that the field is probably uniform.

    (b) Determine the components of the potential gradients in directions along the sides of the cuboid, then add them as vectors to find the magnitude and direction of the electric field in that region of space.

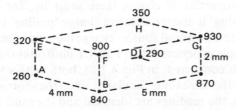

Fig. 3.12   Potential distribution for Problem 3.4.

4 Charge and Electric Flux

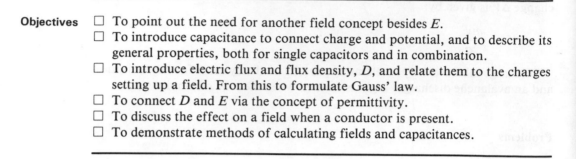

Objectives

☐ To point out the need for another field concept besides E.
☐ To introduce capacitance to connect charge and potential, and to describe its general properties, both for single capacitors and in combination.
☐ To introduce electric flux and flux density, D, and relate them to the charges setting up a field. From this to formulate Gauss' law.
☐ To connect D and E via the concept of permittivity.
☐ To discuss the effect on a field when a conductor is present.
☐ To demonstrate methods of calculating fields and capacitances.

You should now have a good appreciation of the terms 'potential gradient' and 'electric field'. They are alternative ways of describing how a small volume (strictly a point) either in space or within a conductor can become altered so that electric charge placed there will feel a force.

The generation of the field has been discussed in terms of potential difference, with little mention of the flow of charge required to establish this p.d. Moreover, the picture of the field is itself incomplete. Although we can relate potential gradient to field, and therefore to force on a charge, we are not yet in a position to say how this field varies from place to place, other than from experimental results. We cannot yet predict field patterns other than very near a conductor, where equipotential surfaces follow the contours of the conductor under electrostatic conditions, and even there we cannot say how close equipotential surfaces marking particular voltages should be, except in the simple case of parallel plates. Finally, we can say nothing about the effect of insulating materials near the point.

By finding the relationship between the electric charge driven on to the conductors setting up the field and the potentials of those conductors, we will be able to complete the picture.

The concept that connects charge and potential is called **capacitance** and a device in which electric fields are set up for the purpose of charge 'storage' is called a **capacitor**. For reasons that will become clear later, effective capacitors need to have large area conductors separated by a small gap.

Devices can be made using electric fields for other purposes, to provide force for instance. Such devices will have capacitance also, of course.

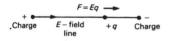

+ and − charges at end of line equal, in fact, but this has not been proved yet.

Capacitance

As a charged particle in an electric field feels a force, then from the original definitions of the properties of charge there must be, for a positive particle, positive charge 'pushing' it and/or negative charge 'pulling' it. So when a field is set up by connection to a potential source, charge movement must occur within the source circuit. A simple experiment like Fig. 4.1 illustrates this.

When the battery is connected, in Fig. 4.1(b), both meters 'kick' by exactly the same amount and for the same time. Similarly, when the short-circuit connection is remade in Fig. 4.1(c), the readings are identical and the same as when the battery was connected, but in the opposite direction.

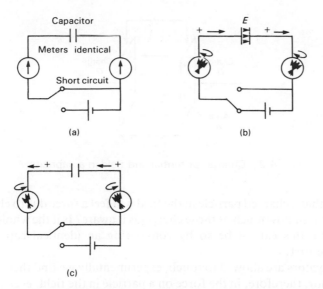

Fig. 4.1 Capacitor charging and discharging.

The short-circuit should be of resistance equal to the internal resistance of the battery for the discharge kick to be identical to the charging kick in all respects except sign.

The results of accurate experiments like these indicate that:

(a) When a capacitor is 'charged', electrons are removed from one plate and piled on to the other in exactly equal numbers.

(b) Regardless of how quickly or slowly the processes take plate, the integrated current flow, or charge, is always the same for a given battery p.d. and plate geometry.

(c) When using batteries of different p.d.s, the charge 'stored' is always found to be proportional to the battery p.d. for capacitors with air gaps.

Result (c) allows us to define a quantity called **capacitance**, which is the amount of charge required to be stored in a capacitive system to raise the p.d. between its conductors by 1 volt. So if a charge of Q coulombs raises the p.d. by V volts:

$$\text{capacitance } C = Q/V \tag{4.1}$$

The unit of capacitance is the coulomb volt^{-1}, which is called the **farad**.

Capacitors are devices made to have a specific capacitance, and will be discussed further in Chapter 5. For the present we will go inside a capacitor, to solve some of the problems set at the beginning of the chapter.

This was originally proved by Michael Faraday with his 'Ice-pail Experiment', though he did not explain it in terms of electrons, of course.

In some cases V is not proportional to Q, in which case the slope capacitance $C_s = dQ/dV$, for small changes in V about a nominal value V_n, is more important:

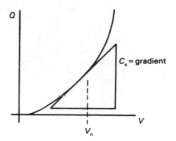

Problem 4.6 continues this idea.

Electric Flux and Permittivity

Charge density and electric fields

Consider a parallel-plate system like the one in Fig. 3.9(b). It is repeated in Fig. 4.2 with some additional information.

We can summarize our present knowledge of this system as follows:

(a) Electric field $E = V/x$ as long as we measure well in from the edge of the plates, from Chapter 3.

(b) charge Q is $\propto$ p.d. V, from earlier work in this chapter.

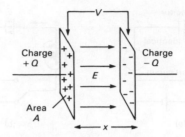

Fig. 4.2   Charge, potential and field in a capacitor.

We know that a charged particle in the field will feel a force due to charges on the two plates, but of how much of those charges is it aware? Is it the whole amount Q?

We can see this cannot be so by considering an identical capacitor placed alongside the first.

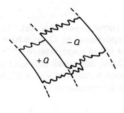

Charged particle

If the capacitors are allowed to touch, experimentally we find there is no change in the field nor, therefore, in the force on a particle in the field, even though twice as much charge exists on each (larger) plate!

If, however, we return to just the original capacitor and double Q on the plates by doubling the battery p.d., we find that this time E doubles also. So the charged particle feels the effect not of the total charge on the plates, but of its concentration or density, not coulombs but coulomb metre^{-2}.

Electric flux density

A pair of charge concentrations, positive on one side of a gap and negative on the other, are inevitably associated with the electric field in the gap. Can we calculate how much charge is needed to match a particular field strength?

This can only be done readily for the parallel-plate case, where the charge concentrations are the same on each side. What happens with cylindrical symmetry, for example?

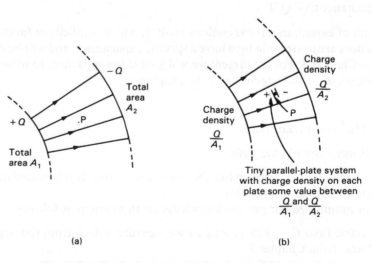

Fig. 4.3   Equivalent charge density and flux density.

The experiments at the beginning of the chapter show that the total charge must be the same on both inner and outer conductor. However, their areas are different so the charge concentrations must be different also. What charge concentration does a charged particle between the plates think exists? Presumably some value intermediate between the concentrations on the outer and inner plates. This value must correspond to the electric field on the particle.

At any point P between the surfaces in Fig. 4.3(a), a charged particle will feel a force. Were the particle instead between parallel plates, in a tiny capacitor, then for it to feel the same force the charge density on the capacitor plates would have to be some value between that on the two cylindrical surfaces. The particle then could not tell the difference between the situation in Fig. 4.3(a) and that in Fig. 4.3(b).

In this simple case, the 'charge density' felt by a particle in the gap follows the spreading out of lines joining positive charges on the inner conductor to equal negative charges on the outer one. For a system with air between the conductors, these lines would follow E lines exactly, though this is not always the case when insulating materials fill the space. The lines joining positive and negative charges are called lines of **electric flux**. The effect of these lines at a point, which leads to an E value at that point, is called **electric flux density**, D. Figure 4.3 can now be redrawn with flux lines, as Fig. 4.4.

Gauss' Law

We will now connect the electric flux density with the charge giving rise to it.

The experiments described at the beginning of this chapter show that the charges on each plate of a capacitive system, which is any system producing an electric field, are equal and opposite. This justifies drawing flux lines within the capacitor starting and finishing on equal and opposite charges.

Electric flux density can be related to the total flux through an area, in exactly the same way as we connected current density J with total current I. To save space, and for revision, the reader is encouraged to work again through the section in Chapter 2 called 'Vector equations for current flow' as far as Eqn(2.17), but this time

'Air' will be used, for familiarity but 'free space', a vacuum, should be considered strictly, as even air has a tiny effect.

Many authors argue that the use of D is unnecessary in the absence of dielectric material, and the 'electrifying effect' can be regarded as E/ϵ, where ϵ is a constant. This makes elementary work slightly easier, but in some insulating materials ϵ not only varies with direction but may cause a change in the direction of the local E. Using D rather than E makes effects like these easier to describe. It was felt that becoming familiar with D before these complications would be helpful.

Often the density is described as '1 line per coulomb', but as the coulomb in a very large charge in electrostatics this may not be helpful. Diagrams of real systems, with a thick mass of lines, probably show 1 line per nanocoulomb or even picocoulomb, but of course this does not make the flux model any less useful.

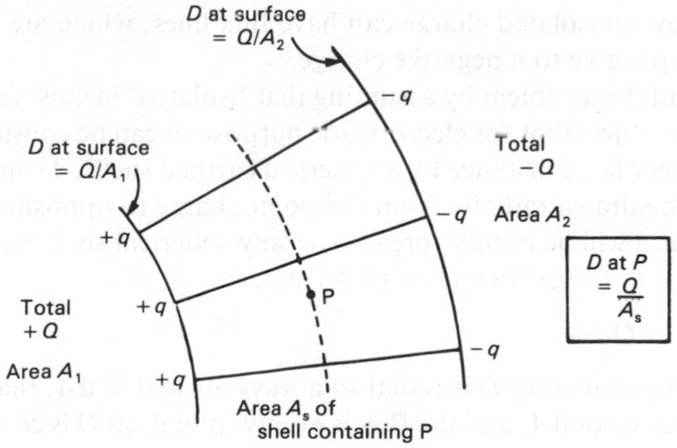

Fig. 4.4   Electric flux density at a point.

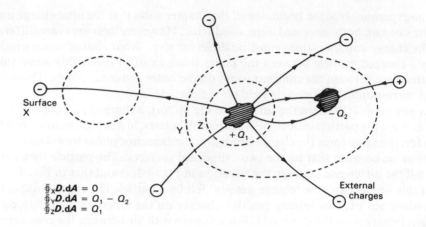

$$\oint_X D.dA = 0$$
$$\oint_Y D.dA = Q_1 - Q_2$$
$$\oint_Z D.dA = Q_1$$

Surface X

$-Q_2$

$+Q_1$

External charges

Fig. 4.5   Illustration of Gauss' law.

replacing 'current flow' by 'electric flux', 'I' by 'Q' as electric flux has the same units as charge and 'J' by 'D'.

Eqn(2.17) becomes translated into:

$$\iint D.dA = \text{total flux through area} \qquad (4.2)$$

We now close the area, by writing the integral as $\oiint$, and note that unlike current flow, which must be equal into and out of a volume, net flux can be produced within a volume, equal to the charge contained within it. If there is no net charge, the enclosing surface integral will be zero, but otherwise:

$$\oiint D.dA = \text{net charge } Q \text{ enclosed by surface } \oiint dA \qquad (4.3)$$

This equation is one expression of **Gauss' law**. (see Fig. 4.5).

Be quite clear that this is not because flux density is the same as current density, but only because it obeys the same mathematical laws and can be pictured by the same intuitive model, therefore.

The alternative form used in more advanced work is the differentiated version: div D = ρ where ρ is volume charge density. Carter, chapter 1, explains this.

Worked Example 4.1

Use Gauss' law to show that the electric flux density produced by an isolated point charge obeys an inverse square law.

Solution: Before the very straightforward mathematics of this problem, we need to establish how an isolated charge can have flux lines, which are supposed to be drawn from a positive to a negative charge.

An earth under electrostatic conditions can have charges on its surface, but it is large enough for these to make no difference to its surface potential. The walls of a room would be an adequate 'distant earth' for a charged ping-pong ball, for instance.

We get round this problem by assuming that 'isolated' means 'far enough away from any other object that for electrostatic purposes it can be considered to be surrounded at a very large distance by a spherical earthed shell'. Then, by symmetry, flux lines can be drawn radially from the point charge to opposite charges on the earthed shell and will be evenly spread over any spherical shell near the charge as shown in Fig. 4.6. Gauss' law [Eqn (4.3)] states:

$$\oiint D.dA = Q$$

In this case by symmetry D is radial so always normal to dA, that is in the same direction as the vector dA, and the flux is evenly spread, so D is constant at a given r. Therefore:

$$D \oiint dA = Q$$

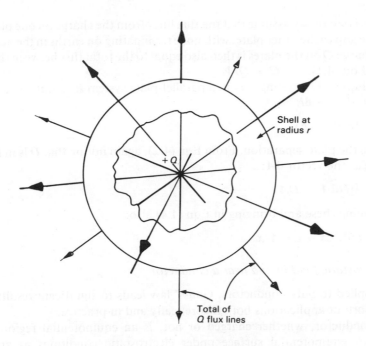

Fig. 4.6 Flux lines from a point charge.

$\oiint d\mathbf{A}$ is simply the surface area of the sphere, so:

$$4\pi r^2 D = Q$$
$$D = Q/4\pi r^2$$

Thus D obeys an inverse square law.

Flux, field and permittivity

As $D \propto Q$ and $E \propto V$ for a system with fixed geometry, and $Q \propto V$ for an air-spaced system, $D \propto E$ also, under these conditions. However, as D and E are quantities defined at a point, this proportionality must be true for all points within all air spaced geometries.

The proportionality constant between D, the flux density caused by charge distribution and geometry, and E, the voltage gradient, in free space is called the **electric constant** and is given the symbol ϵ_0 (epsilon nought).

When insulating materials are placed in an electric field the ratio of D to E is changed, as will be discussed in detail in Chapter 5. To describe this, a constant called **relative permittivity**, ϵ_r, is introduced as a multiplier.

This is all summarized in the equation:

$$D = \epsilon_0 \epsilon_r E \tag{4.4}$$

ϵ_r is equal to 1 for free space and, to a close approximation, for air.

The **capacitance of a parallel-plate capacitor** follows immediately from this equation combined with Eqn(4.1), Eqn(4.2) and Eqn(3.12). We do need to make one further assumption beyond ignoring end-effects, however. If the gap between

ϵ_0 is also called the permittivity of free space.

Strictly, only material along the same flux line as the point under consideration has any effect.

If this is compared with the answer to Worked Example 4.1, it is clear that E produced by a point charge also obeys an inverse square law.

To allow for materials for which E is not in the same direction as D, ϵ_r can be a quantity called a tensor, which affects the direction as well as the magnitude of any vector operated on.

the plates is small, we assume that the flux lines from the charge on one plate all go across the gap to the other plate, with none terminating on earths in the neighbourhood. Charge Q on the plates is then also equal to the total flux between the plates.

From Eqn (4.1): $C = Q/V$

From Eqn (3.12): noting that in a parallel-plate system E is uniform and in the same direction as $\mathbf{d}l$:

$$V = \int E.\mathbf{d}l = Ex$$

where x is the plate separation. From Eqn (4.2), again noting that D is in the same direction as the vector $\mathbf{d}A$:

$$Q = \iint D\mathbf{d}A = DA$$

Combining these and bringing in Eqn (4.4) also:

$$C = DA/Ex = \epsilon_0\epsilon_r A/x \tag{4.5}$$

The electrostatic field in and near a conductor

When applied to bulk conductors, Gauss' law leads to significant results, which have important applications both theoretically and in practice.

Any conductor, whether charged or not, is an equipotential region and its surface an equipotential surface under electrostatic conditions as argued in Chapter 3.

Consider first a solid conductor. No E lines can exist in it, as there can be no potential difference across it. Therefore no D lines can exist in it either. Within the conductor, there can be no charge, therefore, by Gauss' law. Any excess positive or negative charge on the conductor can only reside on its surface.

Consider an uncharged solid conductor in an electric field as shown in Fig. 4.7(a).

D lines begin and end on charge, so charge must move within the conductor as shown. This is called **electrostatic induction**, and can be demonstrated experimentally. The induced charges will distort the field locally as shown in Fig. 4.7(a),

The E field in a gap of, say 0.01 mm will be much greater than between one plate and an earth a few centimetres away.

The distortion can be understood if you remember that E lines (and therefore D lines in air) show the direction a positive charge will move.

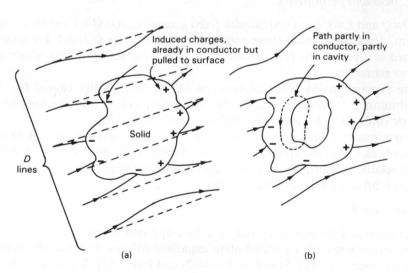

Fig. 4.7 Conductor in an electric field.

where the dashed lines represent the field before the conductor was put in. Conductors tend to concentrate field lines, and therefore strengthen the field near them. Lightning conductors work on this principle, as a pointed conductor will concentrate the field very effectively. In the strong field of an electric storm, breakdown of the air is more likely to occur near a metal point, so lightning can be directed to a safe path.

If there is a cavity within the conductor, as shown in Fig. 4.7(b), we can draw a path partly through conductor and partly through cavity, as shown. As $\oint E.dl = 0$, and we know there can be no E within the conductor, it follows that there can be no E in the space either, as an infinite number of such lines can be drawn, involving all the space. So there can be no electric field in a cavity in a conductor.

This explains why anything requiring protection or 'screening' against electrostatic fields is enclosed within a conductor. Delicate electronic equipment operates in metal boxes, wires carry low-level signals on the inner wire of coaxial cable and even people repairing high-voltage equipment are protected by 'Faraday cages'. For similar reasons you must use an external aerial if you wish to operate a radio in a car or metal-clad caravan.

For details on atmospheric discharges see, for example, Feynman vol 2, chapter 9, or Bolton, chapter 7.

Looking for an electric field within a charged conductor and failing to find it is the best test we have of Gauss' law and the constancy of ϵ_0. See *Phys.Review* (1936), **50**, p. 1066, for Plimpton's and Lawton's experimental work, showing that these bases are true to better than 1 part in 10^9

Worked Example 4.2

A tachometer measures speed of rotation.

A tachometer consists of a pair of fixed parallel plates each of quadrant shape and separated by a 1 mm gap, as shown in Fig. 4.8(a).

Within the gap rotates an earthed vane, also in the form of a pair of quadrants and of thickness 0.2 mm; as it rotates it alternately fills and vacates the space between the fixed quadrants.

The fixed quadrants are connected to a d.c. supply giving potentials of ± 50 V symmetrically either side of earth, and in the same circuit is a device for measuring any current flow to or from the fixed plates. The vane area exposed to the field between the plates totals 1000 mm².

(a) Determine the charge on the fixed plates (i) with the moving vane outside the gaps and (ii) with the moving vane between the fixed plates as shown in Fig. 4.8(b). Ignore electric flux leakage.

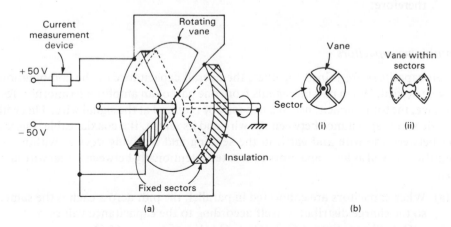

Fig. 4.8 Electrostatic tachometer design.

(b) Describe the waveform of current against time when the vane rotates at f complete revolutions per second and show that the current if rectified would be proportional to the rotation frequency.

Ignore end effects and stray capacitances.

Solution:

(a) (i) This will be a straightforward application of Eqns(4.2), (3.4) and (4.4). From Eqn (4.2):

$$Q = \iint \mathbf{D} \cdot \mathbf{dA} = DA$$

for parallel flux lines. As $D = \epsilon_0 \epsilon_r E$, from Eqn (4.4) and $E = -\mathrm{d}V/\mathrm{d}x = V/x$ for parallel plates (Eqn 3.4):

$$\begin{aligned} Q &= \epsilon_0 \epsilon_r VA/x \\ &= 8.85 \times 10^{-12} \times 1 \times 10^{-3} \times 100/10^{-3} \\ &= 8.85 \times 10^{-10} \text{ C} \end{aligned}$$

In practice, stray capacitance between plates and nearby earths would increase this by a few per cent. The answer to part (b) would be little affected, though.

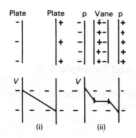

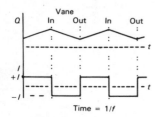

For details about the rectification of a.c. signals see Horowitz and Hill, chapter 1.

(ii) In the figure in the margin, it should be clear that the path length for E lines will be reduced with the vane in the gap, as there is no p.d. across the vane itself. For the same p.d., E will be larger, so will D therefore and as a result so will be Q. The calculation in (i) could be repeated, but as all the relationships are linear we can simply state that Q will be larger in the same ratio that the gap has been effectively reduced:

New value of $Q = 8.85 \times 10^{-10} \times 1/0.8 = 11.06 \times 10^{-10}$ C

(b) As the vane rotates, the charge Q will change in a linear way as shown in the figure in the margin. Current I is the rate of change of Q. As the gradient of the graph of Q against time is constant, so will be I, taking alternately positive and negative values as shown. Because there are two quadrants, there will be two cycles of current waveform each rotation, so each change in Q occupies $1/4f$ seconds:

$$\begin{aligned} I = \mathrm{d}Q/\mathrm{d}t &= (11.06-8.85) \times 10^{-10}/(1/4f) \\ &= 8.84f \times 10^{-10} \text{ A} = 88.4f \text{ nA} \end{aligned}$$

After rectification, a d.c. current proportional to f would be produced, therefore.

Combining capacitors

A.C. voltages can 'drive' currents through capacitance, as will be discussed briefly in Chapter 5 and explained in terms of 'displacement current' in Chapter 11. Yorke, chapter 2, covers the circuit theory aspects.

When capacitors are joined together, the overall capacitance of the combination may be needed. When passing signals from one part of an amplifier to another, for instance, the total capacitance to earth may be required at the signal wire. This will include stray capacitance between the wire and its screen, if a coaxial cable is used, and between the wire and earth in the sending and receiving devices within the amplifier, as well as any capacitors connected intentionally between signal wire and earth.

(a) When capacitors are connected in parallel, the p.d. across each is the same, so the charge distributes itself according to the capacitance values;

Overall capacitance $C = (Q_1 + Q_2)/V = C_1 + C_2$ (4.6)

(b) When they are connected in series, the plates x and y and the wire between behave like the conductor in Fig 4.7, and induced charges appear on the intermediate plates. If the capacitors are large area plates in close proximity, all the flux lines produced by charge Q will cross the gaps, so equal and opposite surface charges appear on x and y, as shown. In this case it is the p.d. that is shared between the capacitors.

Overall capacitance $C = Q/(V_1 + V_2)$

so $1/C = (V_1 + V_2)/Q = 1/C_1 + 1/C_2$ (4.7)

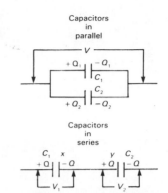

Calculations in Electrostatics

At this relatively elementary level, most calculations in electrostatics are fairly straightforward as long as the following points are borne in mind:

(a) Look for symmetry in any problem. Often you can predict the shape of flux/field lines or of equipotential surfaces very easily, and this can determine the next calculation step.
(b) Remember that flux goes with surface areas whereas potential goes with motion along field or (in air) flux lines.

A strategy is summarized in Fig. 4.9.

For instance, to find a capacitance, you may have to put a known charge somewhere in the system and follow the arrows through the diagram until you have found the potential this charge has caused.

Note on remembering these: the larger the capacitance, the easier it must be to produce electric flux from a given p.d. When capacitors are added in parallel, extra paths for flux are provided, so the resulting capacitance must be bigger. When added in series, flux paths have become longer, so a bigger voltage is required for the same flux. Flux is harder to make so $1/C$s must be added, as $1/C$ represents 'difficulty' whereas C represents 'ease' of making flux. See also the marginal note just before Eqn(2.9).

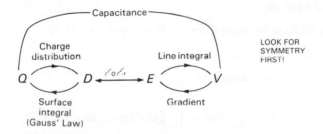

Fig. 4.9   Electrostatics calculations diagram.

Find the capacitance per metre of uniradio no.M203 coaxial cable, which is made up of an inner conductor of diameter 1.12 mm, an outer conductor of diameter 6.25 mm, the space between being taken up by polythene of relative permittivity 1.7.

  Solution: Figure 4.10 shows the arrangement. We put a charge Q on length a of the inner conductor, then calculate the p.d. V this sets up between inner and outer conductor. The capacitance C of this length will be Q/V and the required answer will be C/a.

  By symmetry, D lines will be radial and evenly spaced. As D lines pass through a larger and larger area, moving from the inner conductor to the outer, the flux

Worked Example 4.3

We can't put charge on the outside as there is no field inside a charged conductor (see above). Note the great similarities between this calculation and Worked Example 3.3.

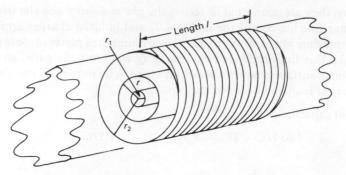

Length l

Fig. 4.10 Coaxial cable for Worked Example 4.3.

density gets less and less, so E decreases also. We need to find how E changes with radius r, so we can integrate w.r.t. r to find V using Eqn(3.12). Following the sequence shown in Fig 4.9:

Gauss' law [Eqn (4.3)] $\qquad Q = \oiint D \cdot \mathbf{d}A$

which when D is always normal to $\mathbf{d}A$, as here:

$$= D \oiint \mathbf{d}A$$
$$= 2\pi\, raD$$
so $\quad D = Q/2\pi\, ra$

Assuming polythene is a linear material (which it is) then [from Eqn (4.4)]:

$$E = D/\epsilon_0\epsilon_r$$
$$= Q/2\pi\,\epsilon_0\epsilon_r\, ra$$

We have our relation between E and r. Now from Eqn (3.12):

$$V = \int E \cdot \mathbf{d}l$$

In this case, E is always along a radius, so:

$$V = \int_{r_1}^{r_2} E\,dr = \int_{r_1}^{r_2} Q\,dr/2\pi\,\epsilon_0\epsilon_r\, ra$$
$$= [Q\ln(r)/2\pi\,\epsilon_0\epsilon_r\, a]_{r_1}^{r_2}$$
$$= Q\ln(r_2/r_1)/2\pi\,\epsilon_0\epsilon_r\, a$$

Capacitance/metre $= Q/Va = 2\pi\,\epsilon_0\epsilon_r/\ln(r_2/r_1)$

With the data in the question:

$$\text{capacitance/metre} = \frac{2 \times \pi \times 8.85 \times 10^{-12} \times 1.7}{\ln(6.25/1.12)} = 55\ \text{pF m}^{-1}$$

However complex the expression, it always has the form:

$$C = \frac{(\text{geometry})\epsilon_0\epsilon_r(\text{an area})}{\text{a length}}$$

or $= (\text{geometry})\epsilon_0\epsilon_r(\text{a length})$

Log quantities are dimensionless. For cylindrical symmetry the geometrical factor is 2π, for spherical symmetry 4π and for plane symmetry π does not appear.

Summary

Systems that generate an electric field are called capacitive systems. The charge Q flowing on to conductors forming such a system causes a potential V to be

46

developed, across the gap between the conductors, given by $C = Q/V$ where C is the capacitance of the system, measured in farads(F).

In a capacitor, E at a point depends on the density D of electric flux, which forms a field whose lines connect $+$ and $-$ charges across the gap. D and E are related by $D = \epsilon_0\epsilon_r E$, where ϵ_0 is the electric constant having a value 8.85×10^{-12} F m^{-1}, and ϵ_r is the relative permittivity of material along the same flux line as the point.

The flux through a surface is related to D at each point (of area dA) on the surface by:

flux $= \iint D.dA$

If a surface completely encloses charge Q, then:

$Q = \oiint D.dA$ This is Gauss's law.

For an isolated charged spherical conductor, or a point charge, D and therefore E also (in air at least) fall off according to an inverse square law. Taking E:

$E = Q/4\pi\epsilon_0 r^2$

The capacitance of a parallel-plate capacitor of area A and plate separation x is given by:

$C = \epsilon_0\epsilon_r A/x$

No field exists inside a conductor under electrostatic conditions, nor in any cavities within a conductor. This is used in the technique of screening.

Capacitances in parallel simply add. For capacitances in series the reciprocals of the individual capacitances are added.

When carrying out calculations, look for symmetry first, then associate flux with surface areas and potentials with field lines.

Problems

*Indicates more challenging problems
Take the electric constant ϵ_0 as 8.85×10^{-12} F m^{-1}.

4.1 A capacitor consists of two parallel plates of area 10^{-2} m^2 and separation 2 mm. It is connected to a 50 V d.c. supply. Calculate, for an increase in separation of 1 mm:
   (a) the change in charge if the supply connections are maintained;
   (b) the change in potential if, instead, the supply connections are broken before the movement takes place.
      Assume parallel-plate conditions in all cases.

4.2 A safety device on a machine must prevent it starting when any earthed object larger than a few cm^2 is nearer than 100 mm to a plate. This plate is 30 mm $\times$ 30 mm and already has a capacitance to earth of 20 pF, including leads and amplifier input. If the plate is charged to 10 V, estimate what change of voltage the amplifier must detect to notice an object at the limit of range. Assume that the capacitance of the plate to this object is equivalent to that of a parallel-plate capacitor of 1/4 the plate area and 100 mm separation and that the charge on the plate remains constant.

4.3 A capacitor in a UHF system consists of two plates, each 15 mm $\times$ 20 mm, separated by 2.5 mm. The plates are mounted centrally within an earthed box, whose top is 10 mm above the upper capacitor plate and whose bottom is 10 mm below the lower one, which is earthed. Assuming the side walls are

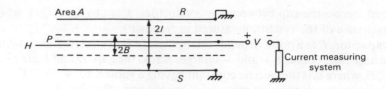

Fig. 4.11   Vibration transducer for Problem 4.5.

distant and ignoring edge effects, estimate the percentage error in basing calculations of capacitance simply on treating the capacitor plates as isolated.

*4.4 Repeat Problem 4.3 but this time consider the two plates to be making equal and opposite potential excursions, instead of the lower plate being earthed.

*4.5 Figure 4.11 represents a vibration transducer. The thin plate P oscillates vertically through a maximum displacement B either side of a plane H halfway between the earthed plates R and S, which are separated by a distance $2l$ and have an area A.

(a) Making the usual parallel-plate assumptions, and ignoring stray effects, show that when P is at a distance x from H its capacitance to earth is given by

$$C = \frac{4\epsilon_0\epsilon_r Al}{4l^2 - x^2}$$

(b) If P oscillates sinusoidally at a frequency ω, show that the current waveform is at a frequency 2ω, and is itself a sinusoid as long as $B \ll 1$.

For details of this process see, for instance, Solymar and Walsh, chapter 9.

4.6 When a semiconductor junction diode is connected in the reverse direction (i.e. so it has very high resistance), a region in it called the depletion zone behaves like a reasonably good insulator of width W, which varies with the applied reverse voltage V according to:

$$W = K\sqrt{(\phi + V)}$$

where K and ϕ are constants. For a particular silicon diode:

$\phi = 0.9$ V
$W = 1.5 \times 10^{-8}$ m when $V = 0$
and $\epsilon_r = 11.8$ for silicon

(a) If the depletion zone can be treated as a parallel-plate capacitor of area 0.05 mm², find the slope capacitance of the diode (i) when $V = 0$ and (ii) when $V = 2.5$ V.

(b) If the electric field across the depletion zone exceeds 10^8 V m^{-1} an effect called zener breakdown occurs. At what applied voltage will this occur in the diode described above?

See Worked Example 4.1 for the interpretation of 'isolated'.

4.7 Show that the capacitance C of an isolated sphere of radius r is given by:

$$C = 4\pi\epsilon_0 r$$

This is the principle of the Van der Graaf generator. For details see, for example, Bolton, chapter 15, Duffin, chapter 5, Nuffield A level Physics Students Guide, New Edition Unit E.

4.8 An electrostatic generator works by collecting charge on to a sphere of radius 0.15 m. From a discharged state, it takes 8 s to build up sufficient electric field at its surface (3000 V mm^{-1}) to begin discharging into the air. Charge is fed at a steady rate by a belt moving into the centre of the sphere (where there is no field, of course).

(a) What is the potential when discharge begins?

(b) What steady current would the generator drive through a meter?

4.9 Find the capacitance of a pair of concentric isolated spheres of radii 10 cm and 40 cm if:

(a) the outer one is earthed;

(b) the inner one is earthed;

(c) as (a) and (b), but with a material of relative permittivity 7 between the spheres.

A somewhat academic question, but a good test of your understanding of *D* and *E* lines.

5 Electric Fields in Materials

☐ To describe electrical polarization simply, at the atomic level, and show how this leads to dielectric behaviour.

☐ To define the behaviour of E and D in dielectrics and introduce the polarization vector P.

☐ To introduce piezoelectricity and electrets.

☐ To discuss dielectric strength and the importance of electrode curvature in causing breakdown.

☐ To derive the force between point charges, the potential near a point charge and the field of a dipole.

☐ To discuss electrostatic energy and energy density and relate them to electrostatic force, applying this to loudspeakers.

☐ To introduce briefly the design and structure of capacitors.

☐ To show how the ideas in Chapters 2 – 5 can lead to an understanding of dust precipitators, xerography, microphones and liquid crystals.

The difference between a conductor and an insulator is usefully described in Carter, chapter 1, in terms of the time taken for charge to distribute itself inside. Times from 10^{-19} s for copper to 10 days for quartz are quoted!

This has been explored in a different context in Problem 4.1.

A material with a relative permittivity ϵ_r greater than 1 is called a dielectric material. The name is probably redundant, as all insulators behave like this, but the behaviour itself is called the dielectric effect, which is a useful name.

As Eqn(4.4) shows, introducing such material into an electric field will cause a reduction of E relative to D. If the p.d. V across a capacitor is kept constant, the charge Q on its plates will increase; if Q is kept constant, V will decrease. The capacitance Q/V will always be increased by the presence of a dielectric, therefore, as Eqn(4.5) shows for the parallel-plate case.

We need to be very clear whether any capacitor we are discussing is connected to a constant-potential battery, which can supply or remove as much charge as is necessary, or whether it is charged and isolated, in which case the p.d. between its plates may change, but not the charge on them.

Polarization and Dielectrics

Models of polarization

It is simpler to understand the effects of dielectric materials and why we define E and D in a certain way within them if we start at the atomic level.

If an electric field is applied to individual atoms or molecules as shown in Fig. 5.1 they distort, or in some cases rotate, so that charges within them are aligned along the field lines.

The effect of this is to create layers on the surface of the dielectric, which act like charges, negative on the left-hand side in Fig. 5.1 and positive on the right. These layers are called 'polarization charges'.

In some cases the alignment is not exact, and a polarization component across the applied field is produced.

Insulators can also pick up a surface charge, by contact or friction, but this would be conducted away if metal were in contact. Polarization 'charges' remain fixed.

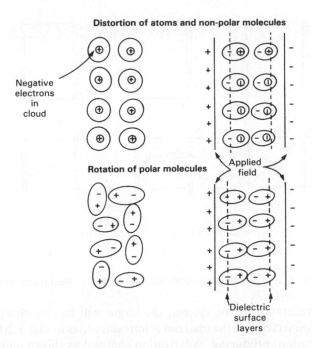

Distortion of atoms and non-polar molecules

Negative
electrons
in
cloud

Rotation of polar molecules

Applied
field

Dielectric
surface
layers

Fig. 5.1   Simple models of polarization at the atomic level.

However, they are not the same as the charges that would appear if a conductor were placed in the field, for two reasons:

(a) The charges cannot be removed, as they are not produced by the motion of free conduction electrons. This could be shown by cutting the material down the middle, while in the field, along a plane parallel to the plates, then removing the cut pieces. If a conductor were used, there would be a net negative charge on the left-hand piece, and positive on the right. For a dielectric, assuming the atoms or molecules cannot be cut through, there is no net charge on either piece.

(b) The quantity of effective charge at the surface is not the same as that on the plates; it is always less.

Because of these differences, we do not apply Gauss' law as defined using D to polarization charges. We could justify this by assuming that any surface we draw through the material does not pass through atoms or molecules. Electric flux lines are therefore only drawn from positive to negative conduction charges.

Flux and field equations in a dielectric

Consider for simplicity a dielectric material almost entirely filling the space between the plates of a parallel-plate capacitor; we can deal with other cases later. If the p.d. is held constant, then by experiment charge flows on to the plates when we insert the dielectric. Refer to Fig. 5.2, where to aid understanding the battery is disconnected while the dielectric material is put in, then reconnected to supply the extra charge.

Figure 5.2(a) show the system without dielectric. The battery sets up a p.d. and charge flows on to the plates until the potential gradient shown is produced; the

Figure 4.7 and Worked Example 4.2 deal with the effect of a conductor within an electric field.

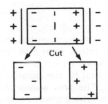

Cut

In some books, such as Carter, chapter 1, Gauss' law is defined with reference to E at first. In this case, polarization charges need to be included, but the ensuing definition involving D still excludes them, and is the same as our Eqn(4.3).

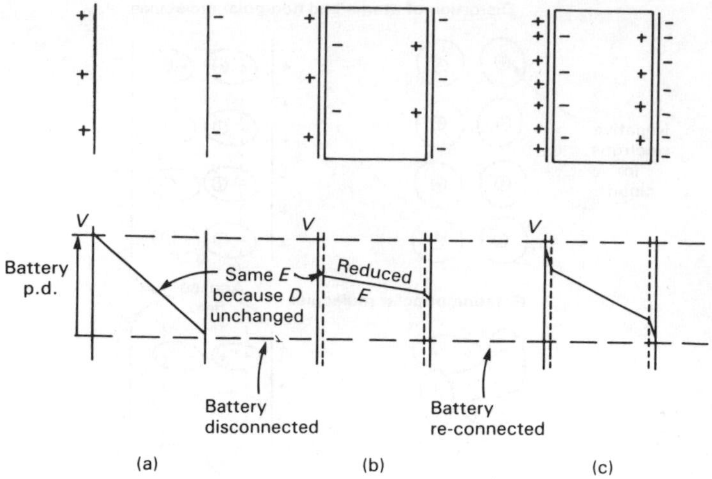

Fig. 5.2 Charge and potential in a partially filled capacitor.

Notice how the concepts of D and E have been manipulated and more closely defined in order to make them fit this new situation. Always remember they are inventions and can be treated exactly as desired, as long as a self-consistent model is produced that maps on to real life accurately.

It is safer to talk about the potential gradient within the material rather than E as force on a charge, which is complicated by the polarization process. The only way a charge could feel the correct value of the force of the E field would be if it were in a very narrow tube the full length of the dielectric. Carter, chapter 2, discusses this problem further.

The effect can be described also in terms of an effective surface charge density, as Carter does in chapter 2.

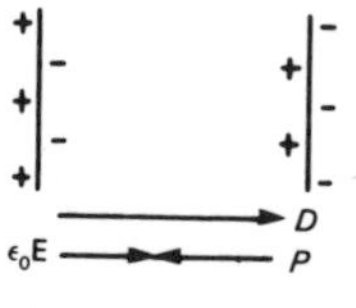

bigger the capacitance of the system, the larger will be this charge. When the battery is disconnected and the material is introduced, as in Fig. 5.2(b), the E field causes polarization, producing 'polarization charges' as shown on its surface. In the tiny gap between plate and dielectric, the flux density is the same as before, as the conduction charge to the right of the left-hand gap is still -3 units. E must therefore also be the same, so the voltage gradient between plate and dielectric will now be as before. Within the dielectric itself, we have a problem with our model; remember D and E are only models! We need to decide how the E field crossing a plane within the material can be related both to the charges on the plates and to the polarization charges, which cannot be removed and are only there because of the applied field, as explained above.

As suggested already, we regard D as fixed by the conduction charges on the plates, so to explain the effect of polarization we introduce another vector, called the **polarization vector**, P, which acts between positive and negative polarization charges and opposes D. The potential gradient across the material results from this opposition, and is therefore less than it would be without the dielectric.

Returning to Fig. 5.2, the potential across the whole capacitor has now been reduced, so when the battery is re-connected further charge must flow in, to increase the p.d. to its former value, as shown in Fig. 5.2(c). The capacitance has therefore increased.

It should be clear that if the tiny gaps between conductor and dielectric are now reduced to zero, the potentials at the polarization charges will arrive at the conductor potentials and even more charge must flow on to the plates.

In summary: when a dielectric material is present, D is connected with the charges on any conductors setting up the field, whereas E is determined from the potential drop across various parts of the system. Any difference between the ratio of D to E and its free space value ϵ_0 is described either by the multiplying factor ϵ_r or by a polarization vector P, which acts in the opposite direction to D. The marginal figure illustrates the equation summarizing the case where dielectric completely fills the space between the conductors:

$$D = \epsilon_0 E + P \tag{5.1}$$

There is a 'chicken and egg' situation here, in that P is caused by E in the first place as only force on a charge can cause the effects seen in Fig. 5.1, but the resulting overall E depends on whether charge is allowed to flow on to the plates in response to P.

Worked Example 5.1

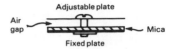

A variable capacitor consists of two plates of area 100 mm², separated by a piece of mica of relative permittivity 7 and thickness 0.1 mm and a variable air gap. Determine the capacitance when the total distance separating the plates is 0.3 mm.

Solution: There are two approaches to simple multiple-dielectric problems, and both will be used by way of illustration:

1st method. The capacitor behaves in effect like two capacitors in series, one (C_1) with a 0.2 mm air gap, the other (C_2) with a 0.1 mm mica gap, so Eqn(4.7) can be used:

$$1/C = 1/C_1 + 1/C_2$$

Using Eqn (4.5):

$$C_1 = 8.85 \times 10^{-12} \times 10^{-4}/(0.2 \times 10^{-3}) = 4.425 \text{ pF}$$
$$C_2 = 8.85 \times 10^{-12} \times 7 \times 10^{-4}/(10^{-4}) = 61.95 \text{ pF}$$

A more general approach, bringing in the behaviour of V, E and D at the boundary, is given in more advanced work, such as Carter, chapter 2, which also discusses the use of energy concepts for this purpose.

Putting these into Eqn (4.7):

$$1/C = 2.26 \times 10^{11} + 1.614 \times 10^{10} = 2.42 \times 10^{11}$$
So $C = 4.13 \text{ pF}$

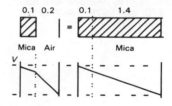

2nd method The potential gradient in air will be 7 times as steep as it will be in mica. Were the capacitor made entirely of mica, the gap at present occupied by air would need to be 7 times thicker to produce the same potential drop. So 0.2 mm air is equivalent to 1.4 mm mica, and the whole capacitor behaves as if made from a thickness of 1.5 mm mica.

So using Eqn (4.5):

$$C = 8.85 \times 10^{-12} \times 7 \times 10^{-4}/(1.5 \times 10^{-3})$$
$$= 4.13 \text{ pF}$$

The second method is quicker and perhaps more aesthetically appealing, but does demand a sure understanding of the effect of dielectrics on D and E fields.

Piezoelectricity and electrets

Certain materials, notably quartz, Rochelle salt (potassium hydrogen tartrate) and barium titanate ceramic, generate polarization charges when their shape is changed. Conversely, their shape changes when an electric field is applied to them. This set of properties is known as **piezoelectricity**.

There are many applications of both effects, which can be divided into three main classes:

Another property, electrostriction, exists but only involves a change of shape in an applied field without its converse.

(a) Electrical-mechanical transducers: high-frequency loudspeakers ('tweeters' and ultrasonic transmitters) couple electrical oscillations into acoustic waves at frequencies from a few kilohertz up to the megahertz range or even higher.
(b) Mechanical-electrical transducers: force, pressure and acceleration sensors

For detailed accounts of these applications consult, for example Solymar and Walsh, chapter 10.

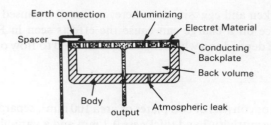

Fig. 5.3   Basic form of electret microphone (courtesy *Brit. Communications Engineering Journal*; first published in POEEJ, Vol 72, Apr 1979).

use piezoelectric crystals, as do the converse devices to those in (a), such as microphones, record player pickups and ultrasonic receivers.

(c) Electrical-electrical transducers: a crystal, often of quartz, is fed with an oscillating electric field. The mechanical vibrations produced may be converted back into electricity either at the same point to induce resonance in a highly accurate oscillator or at another point to act as a signal delaying device.

A further, and expanding, application is the generating of surface acoustic waves (SAW) which can alter the optical properties of a crystal and allow the processing of information contained in light beams.

A material replacing delicate piezoelectric crystals for some applications is the **electret**. A plastic sheet is chosen whose molecules are strongly polar, having well-separated positive and negative regions. In one method of polarization the plastic is softened by heat and then cooled, all the while in a strong electric field. The polarization induced by the field, by molecule rotation, is thus 'frozen in' and the material can be cut into suitable shapes to act as the diaphragm of a capacitive microphone as illustrated in Fig. 5.3.

Capacitive microphones will be studied again later in this chapter.

Dielectric strength and field patterns for discharge

If the electric field across a dielectric is increased, eventually a form of catastrophic breakdown occurs. Avalanche breakdown in a gas has been described in Chapter 3. For a solid, a similar phenomenon takes place when electrons, liberated as electron-hole pairs, can acquire enough speed between collisions to generate further EHPs.

The *E* field magnitude to do this is called the **Dielectric strength** of the material. For air under everyday conditions it has a value of $3000 \, \mathrm{kV \, m^{-1}}$, although for most solid dielectrics it is appreciably larger. Thus insulators rather than air gaps are used when high potentials are generated.

If breakdown is to be either avoided, in high-voltage equipment, or encouraged, in lightning conductors or discharge tubes, the electric field near a conductor needs to be tailored to ensure respectively either minimum or maximum values at a required potential.

Consider an isolated conductor with a fixed charge on it. If the conductor is spherical, flux lines must be evenly distributed, whereas if it has a protuberance this will not be so. This can be argued intuitively from Fig. 5.4.

The surface of the conductor is equipotential. At a very great distance from the

See *POEEJ*, **72**, Apr, 1979, pp. 15–18; *JAc.Soc.Am*, **53**(6), 1973, pp. 1578–1587 for further details.

'Electron-hole pair' is usually abbreviated to EHP.

See Worked Example 4.1 for an explanation of 'isolated'.

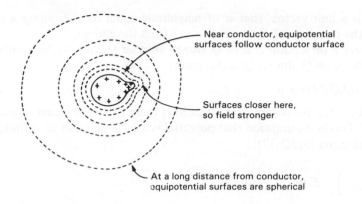

Fig. 5.4 Equipotential surfaces near a non-spherical charged conductor.

conductor, the equipotential surfaces will be spherical, so as one moves inwards the surfaces will change their shape from spherical to fit the conductor surface. The surfaces must be closer together near the protuberance, therefore, and so the E field will be stronger there. So also must be the D field and thus the charge density at the surface of the conductor·must be greatest at the protuberance.

Two practical points follow from this:

(a) For a given charge on a surface of given area, the E field just above the surface will be a minimum for a sphere, where no one region has a greater charge density than any other. As, moreover, the capacitance of an isolated sphere goes as the radius while its surface area goes as radius squared, the surface charge density for a given potential decreases with sphere radius. This means the D field and therefore E field just above the surface will also decrease with radius. Thus large spherical conductors are used to reduce the possibility of discharge in high-potential systems, from TV electron gun supplies up to mains transformers for the National Grid system.

(b) The surface E field will be a maximum on a conductor where the curvature is a maximum, that is the radius of curvature is a minimum. Thus points are used for lightning conductors to direct a strike to safe conducting path by increasing the field locally.

Electrostatic force and Energy

We begin with Eqn(3.1), the fundamental force law of electrostatics:

$$F = QE$$

Forces and fields due to single charges and dipoles

It has already been shown that the D field produced by a point charge obeys an inverse square law. Eqn (4.4) connects D with E, so in free space we may write for the E field at a distance r from a point charge Q:

$$E = (Q/4\pi\epsilon_0 r^2)\hat{r} \tag{5.2}$$

This can be justified by using the fact that the field of a spherical charge obeys an inverse square law, whereas that of a dipole falls off as an inverse cube. Worked Example 5.2 proves the latter.

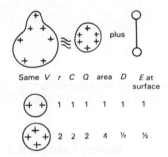

	Same	V	r	C	Q	area	D	E at surface
		1	1	1	1	1	1	1
		2	2	2	4	½	½	

See also Problem 4.7

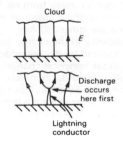

In Worked Example 4.1, by symmetry the field outside an isolated spherical conductor would be the same as that of a point charge. Inside it would be zero, of course.

where $\hat{r}$ is a unit vector, that is of magnitude equal to one, along a radius, to indicate the direction of E, which is away from the charge.

The force F on a point charge Q_1 due to another Q_2 and, by Newton's reaction law, the force on Q_2 due to Q_1 is therefore:

$$F = (Q_1 Q_2/4\pi\epsilon_0 r^2)\hat{r} \qquad (5.3)$$

This goes right back to Coulomb's original experiments, measuring the forces on charged pith balls in 1785.

From Eqn(5.2) the potential at a location r from a charged sphere or point can be obtained. On the assumption that potential is zero at an earth an infinite distance away, and using Eqn(3.12):

$$V = -\int_{\infty}^{r} E.dl$$

which with spherical symmetry becomes:

$$V = -\int_{\infty}^{r} E\,dr$$

$$= -\int_{\infty}^{r} (Q/4\pi\epsilon_0 r^2)\,dr$$

$$= -[-Q/4\pi\epsilon_0 r]_{\infty}^{r}$$

$$= Q/4\pi\epsilon_0 r \qquad (5.4)$$

So the potential falls off according to an inverse unity law. This makes for very straightforward calculations of the potential due to assemblages of point charges. Calculations of the field are more difficult, as the individual fields require to be added as vectors.

Remember the potential is uniform across a conductor.

Care needs to be taken when considering assemblages of conductors, as electrostatic induction will take place due to the field of each acting on the others.

Worked Example 5.2

A dipole consists of equal positive and negative charges separated in space. Find the tangential and radial components of the electric field at a distance r from the midpoint of the dipole, E_r and E_θ in Fig 5.5(a). Show that when r is large compared with the dipole separation $2a$ each component falls off according to an inverse cube law.

This is why the equipotential surfaces far away from an isolated charged object of any shape are spherical. Any asymmetry in the charge can be represented by dipoles added to an overall spherical charge. The dipole effects decay much faster with distance, leaving only the inverse square law symmetry. See marginal figure after Fig. 5.4.

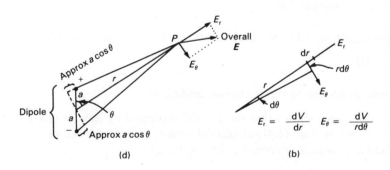

Fig. 5.5   Field near an electrostatic dipole.

Solution: Figure 5.5(a) shows the arrangement and the approximations justified by r being $\gg 2a$.

We shall use Eqn(5.4) and differentiate it to find the field. Note from Fig. 5.5(b) that as V has to be differentiated w.r.t. a displacement, r will be involved in E_θ.

$$\text{Net } V \text{ at } P = (V \text{ due to } + \text{ charge}) - (V \text{ due to } - \text{ charge})$$

$$= \frac{Q}{4\pi\,\epsilon_0}\left(\frac{1}{r - a\cos\theta} - \frac{1}{r + a\cos\theta}\right)$$

$$= \frac{Q}{4\pi\,\epsilon_0}\left(\frac{2a\cos\theta}{r^2 - a^2\cos^2\theta}\right)$$

$$\text{which for } a \ll r = \frac{Q}{2\pi\,\epsilon_0}\left(\frac{a\cos\theta}{r^2}\right)$$

Differentiating to find E_r and E_θ:

$$E_r = -\,\mathrm{d}V/\mathrm{d}r = Qa\cos\theta/6\pi\,\epsilon_0 r^3$$
$$E_\theta = -\,\mathrm{d}V/r\mathrm{d}\theta = Qa\sin\theta/2\pi\,\epsilon_0 r^3$$

Thus each component falls off with an inverse cube law. So would the net field **E** also, therefore.

Electrostatic energy

As potential is the energy of unit charge, the energy of an electrostatic system is likely to be found from adding products of potential and charge.

For a fixed charge $\mathrm{d}Q$ moving from potential V_1 to potential V_2, assuming $\mathrm{d}Q$ is so small that it does not affect the potential distribution, the energy given to $\mathrm{d}Q$ is simply $(V_2 - V_1)\mathrm{d}Q$. This is adequate for the acceleration of electrons, for instance, where the particles being given energy have no noticeable effect on the accelerating electrodes. In many cases, though, substantial charge is transferred from a lower to a higher potential, or vice versa, and this transfer will itself cause a change in potential; alternatively, a battery will need to provide or remove charge to keep the potential constant. Looking at these two problems in turn:

(a) If an isolated capacitor has a p.d. V between its plates, and a small charge $\mathrm{d}Q$ is transferred from one plate to the other, the energy input $\mathrm{d}W$ is given by:

$$\mathrm{d}W = V\mathrm{d}Q \tag{5.5}$$

For a linear system, V will be related to the charge Q at present on the plates by the usual equation $Q = CV$ so:

$$\mathrm{d}W = Q\mathrm{d}Q/C \tag{5.6}$$

If a substantial charge transfer takes place, altering the charge on the plates from Q_1 to Q_2, the energy change ΔW will be given by:

$$\Delta W = \int_{Q_1}^{Q_2} Q\mathrm{d}Q/C \tag{5.7}$$

So a charged capacitor has potential energy W given by:

> Adding up products in this context is integration, of course, as discussed in the Appendix.

Don't try to remember all of these; remember one and work out the others from Eqn(4.1).

$$W = \int_0^Q QdQ/C = Q^2/2C = CV^2/2 = QV/2 \qquad (5.8)$$

(b) If a battery maintains the potential V across a capacitor, any charge transferred from one plate to the other must pass through the battery. Eqn(5.5) still applies, but V is constant, so to transfer charge Q requires simply $W = VQ$. In this case, the capacitor gains energy equal to $QV/2$, but there is a net loss of energy from the system.

Worked Example 5.3

There are many cases where a complicated equation can be applied and used, not necessarily with any physical understanding, whereas a good intuitive grasp of the problem can suggest a neater and shorter way. In this case you could apply the exponential expressions for practice or if you wish to confirm these simple results.

This applies even when a charged capacitor is discharged into another capacitor, which can also damage switch contacts. It also has an important bearing on the power consumed by CMOS logic circuits, as used in watches and calculators. Very little d.c. current flows under steady conditions, but at high frequencies stray capacitances are being continually charged and discharged. The power loss is approximately proportional to frequency even though a capacitor stores energy without loss!

A 6 V battery is used with a switch to charge up a 1000 μF capacitor through a resistance of 10 kΩ. How much energy is dissipated in the resistance? What is the answer if a resistance of 100 kΩ is used? Discuss also the case when the circuit resistance is very low.

Solution: If you are adept at using the exponential decay formulae for CR circuits, it is a fairly straightforward waste of time to set up the charging equations and integrate to find the energy. However, the discussions above make for a much easier calculation!

As far as the capacitor is concerned, charge flows on to it until its potential rises from 0 to 6 V, so one of the Eqns (5.8) must be used such as $W = QV/2$. The battery, however, supplies a constant p.d., so its energy output is equal to QV. The resistor must, therefore, dissipate the difference between these two quantities, $QV/2$. So when a capacitor is charged from a fixed potential, exactly half the energy from the potential source is wasted as heat.

In the example, energy lost in resistor $= QV/2$
$$= CV^2/2$$
$$= 1000 \times 10^{-6} \times 36/2$$
$$= 18 \text{ mJ}$$

The resistance does not enter the calculation, so it must be irrelevant. Its only effect is on the rate of transfer of energy, the power dissipated at any instant.

If the circuit resistance is very low, much of it would be in the thin oxide layer on the switch contacts. When the switch is closed, most of the 18 mJ would be dissipated in these contacts, therefore. In cases where even more energy is involved, a switch could be destroyed very quickly, so care is needed to ensure the presence of enough resistance when large capacitors are charged.

When potential energy is contained within a battery, we can identify it with the chemicals that start to react together when the battery drives current. When the energy is stored within a capacitor, where is it? Is it in the charges, or perhaps the space between the plates?

If the capacitor contains a dielectric, the energy could be regarded as being in the distorted atoms when they are polarized, though even this begs the question, as there is space between the distorted electron shells and the inner parts of the atoms!

Carter, chapter 8, involves a detailed discussion of the energy in an electromagnetic wave.

We could say that the energy is stored in the charges on the plates, but the quantity of energy depends on the spacing between the plates also. When you meet electromagnetic waves in later courses, you will find that electric fields can exist with no charge as their immediate cause, yet those fields can apply force to charged particles and accelerate them, so they must contain energy. Their energy can only be in the space they occupy.

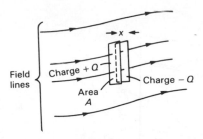

Fig. 5.6 Equivalent capacitor in an electric field.

We will assume, therefore, that when a region of space contains an electric field it contains energy also, related to the energy required to set up that field, and expressible in terms of E and/or D.

Calculating the energy within a region can be done for a general case using advanced vector methods. Here we shall take a parallel-plate example and argue that if we can find the energy density, by making the parallel-plate system as small as we like, we can then integrate to find the energy in any real situation.

In a region, which may or may not include dielectric material, where there exists a flux density D and voltage gradient E, consider a small parallel-plate capacitor with charges on it which reproduce exactly those D and E values as in Fig. 5.6.

The energy stored in the tiny capacitor $= Q^2/2C$

$$= D^2A^2x/2\epsilon_0\epsilon_r A$$

$$= \epsilon_0\epsilon_r E^2 Ax/2 \qquad (5.9)$$

Thus $\epsilon_0\epsilon_r E^2/2$ represents the **energy stored per unit volume** in an electric field. This will be a useful result when we look at capacitor design shortly.

Electrostatic force

The simplest calculations involving electrostatic force are those covered already, where a constant charge Q exists in a constant electric field E. In this case force $F = QE$.

In any other case, the force could be obtained by using Eqn(5.3) and summing the forces on all charges by all other charges, but that is impractical in many cases.

Often a force is produced under non-linear conditions, where movement may alter its size. If the potential energy can be calculated for any state of a system, the relation between force and potential energy change, $F = -dW/dx$, can be used. We assume the energy change dW resulting from a displacement dx is so small that the value of F can be taken as constant. This method is essential when forces produced by increasing polarization are considered, for instance if dielectric is allowed to move between capacitor plates. It will be needed for some calculations in magnetism also.

Figure 5.7 shows a proposed silent variable filter system for use with a spotlight for a very small set in a TV natural history studio.

When the p.d. V is applied the coloured liquid L rises between the mica plates P, colouring the light in a controlled way, with no mechanical noise. The mica plates

Carter, chapter 2, gives a more advanced account of energy storage in an electric field and its use in problem-solving.

We have used this idea of quantity at a point already, in Chapters 2 and 4.

For this simple expression to apply in a dielectric, D must be in the same direction as E, in other words the dielectric must be isotropic. The energy density can be shown to equal $\int E.dD$ in the most general case, as Carter, chapter 2, shows.

Worked Example 5.4

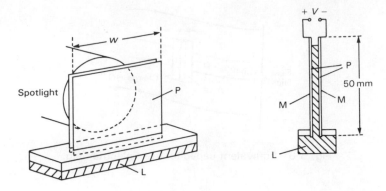

Fig. 5.7 Electrostatic spotlight filter for Worked Example 5.4.

That is, the contact angle is 90°.

have a transparent metal film M on their outside, to set up the electric field. The plates are 0.1 mm thick and the liquid channel 1 mm wide. The relative permittivity of mica is 6 and the liquid, which is aqueous, has a relative permittivity of 80 and a density of 1000 kg m^{-3}. The mica is treated so the surface tension of the liquid has no effect. Calculate the p.d. V required to raise the liquid the full 50 mm up the channel. Take g as 10 N kg^{-1}.

Solution: This can only be solved by using $F = -dW/dx$, so we need to obtain an expression for the system potential energy for a particular height h of liquid. this can be differentiated to find the force at that height in terms of V. Knowing the weight of liquid to be supported at that height we can find V in terms of h and hence the answer.

The energy will have to be calculated for each material above and below the liquid surface. There are several valid approaches, but the most straightforward is probably to calculate the capacitance of each part of the system.

Let the overall width be w, as in Fig. 5.7. With the liquid at height h we have two capacitors in parallel.

Below the liquid surface the dielectric consists of 0.2 mm mica and 1 mm liquid. Using method 2 from Worked Example 5.1, this is equivalent to $1 + (0.2 \times 80/6)$ = 3.67 mm liquid.

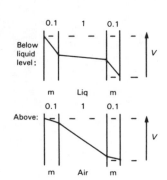

Capacitance of region below liquid surface:

$$= \frac{8.85 \times 10^{-12} \times 80 \times h \times w}{3.67 \times 10^{-3}}$$
$$= 1.93 \times 10^{-7}hw$$

Above the surface the dielectric is 0.2 mm mica and 1 mm air, which is equivalent to $0.2 + (1 \times 6) = 6.2$ mm mica.

Capacitance of region above liquid surface:

$$= \frac{8.85 \times 10^{-12} \times 6\,(0.05-h) \times w}{6.2 \times 10^{-3}}$$
$$= 8.56 \times 10^{-9}\,(0.05-h)\,w$$

Total potential energy:

$$W = CV^2/2$$
$$= (1.93 \times 10^{-7}h + 8.56 \times 10^{-9}(0.05-h))wV^2/2$$
$$= (1.84 \times 10^{-7}h + 4.28 \times 10^{-10})wV^2/2$$

From the arguments just before Worked Example 5.3, the system as a whole loses the same amount of potential energy as the capacitor gains, so a plus sign can be used in the expression for force:

$$\text{Force} = dW/dh$$

where W is the capacitor energy, equal to the loss in total energy, as it is connected to a battery:

$$= 9.22 \times 10^{-8}wV^2$$

$$\text{Weight of column of liquid} = \text{volume} \times \text{density} \times g$$
$$= 10^{-3}hw \times 1000 \times 10$$

For $h = 0.05$ m (full height of cell):

$$9.22 \times 10^{-8}V^2 = 10 \times 0.05$$
so $$V = 2.3 \text{ kV}$$

The author has not tried this out, but the figures suggest it could be made to work. Coating the mica and protecting the liquid from evaporation would be the main problems, along with working at over 2 kV. The liquid would need to be de-ionized! An organic liquid might be better, though a much higher p.d. would then be needed to compensate for the lower ϵ_r.

Repeat the calculation in Worked Example 5.4 with a cell ten times larger in each linear dimension.
(Answer: $v = 74$ kV)

Exercise 5.1

Because ϵ_0 is such a small quantity, electrostatic forces are not large. Worked Example 5.4 showed that to achieve very modest forces, relatively high potentials are needed, albeit supplying small currents. Moreover, the larger the system, the harder it is to operate at all with electrostatics. This is because electrostatic fields are generated by a surface density of charge and most bodies intended to be acted upon by fields themselves carry a surface charge rather than charge distributed through their volume. Inertia and weight, however, depend on the volume of objects. If a system using electrostatic force is made to work, and then scaled up, say 10 times in linear dimensions, its area will be 100 times bigger but its volume will have increased by 1000 times. Thus any electrostatic forces will have only 1/10 of the effect they had in the smaller system. Exercise 5.1 asked you to scale up Worked Example 5.4 as an illustration; you may have been surprised by the answer you found!

This is not true at the atomic level, where electrostatic forces provide the chemical bonding between atoms and molecules. When distances are even smaller (see Problem 5.5), the inverse square law provides for very large forces.

Luckily, scaling effects in magnetism work in exactly the opposite way: the larger the system the better it works, as will be made clear later. In general, large electrical machines, like motors and generators, work by magnetism, whereas small ones, like the tails of bacteria, use electrostatics.

Electrostatic loudspeakers

Electrostatic loudspeakers, however, are something of an exception, as they can be quite sizeable. In a sense, though, they prove the rule, as they work successfully just because they are a large area/low inertia system. A powerful loudspeaker must couple a relatively small motion to a large mass of air. A big sheet of thin metal or metallised film, acted upon by electrostatic forces supplied by a nearby plate or plates, might be expected to work well.

For details of this fascinating discovery, see *Nature* 1975, April, p. 389, and *Scientific American* 1978, March, p. 110.

A good loudspeaker should be efficient, in coupling a high percentage of the input energy into air vibration, and also very linear. Important information within sounds is contained in small alterations in wave shape, and the ear is very sensitive to these subtleties. Any system that adds noticeable distortion will therefore be quite unsatisfactory for sound reproduction.

It turns out that because of this, the simplest method of converting potential into sound, by making one plate of a capacitor mobile and varying the charge on it, cannot be used.

Using the usual abbreviations for plate area etc.:

$$\text{Potential energy of capacitor} = CV^2/2$$
$$= \epsilon_0 A V^2/2x$$

When force is calculated, by differentiating w.r.t. x, it will come out to be proportional to V^2/x^2. If V is increased the plates will move together, presumably against a spring, but the reduction in x will mean that the next identical increase in V will have more effect so the system is non-linear. In theory a square-law spring could be designed, but it would not be easy, and there are better ways to linearize the force.

If a charged sheet is suspended between the plates of a capacitor, using a linear sprung support to keep it central, a linear system results, as long as the charge on the sheet is kept constant and the electrostatic force is produced by applying a p.d. to the capacitor plates. In this case a field E is set up, and the sheet responds simply according to $F = QE$.

To keep the sheet charged it must be maintained at a high potential. However, if the sheet is merely connected to a constant voltage supply, charge will flow when the sheet moves, as its capacitance to the external plates will vary, thus we would have a nonlinear system once more! The solution is to insert a resistance between supply and sheet, large enough so that negligible charge flows during even the slowest cycle of the signal waveform used.

Figure 5.8 shows the construction of an electrostatic loudspeaker, and Problem 5.4 at the end of the chapter pursues some of the ideas further.

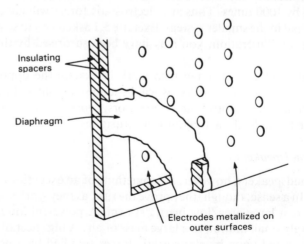

Insulating spacers

Diaphragm

Electrodes metallized on outer surfaces

Fig. 5.8   Structure of an electrostatic loudspeaker.

Capacitor Design

At this point we bring together the ideas you have studied in electrostatics and use them in the most frequently encountered application of the subject, the capacitor. As the details of circuit design using capacitors can be found elsewhere, only a hint follows:

See, for example, Yorke, chapter 2.

Capacitors do not conduct (or only to a minute degree if a less than perfect insulator is used as the dielectric), so a d.c. potential difference can be maintained across them with no current flow occurring. If the p.d. is altered, current will flow while it is changing, according to the differentiated form of Eqn(4.1) which for a constant capacitance becomes:

$$I = C dV/dt \qquad (5.10)$$

Thus current flows in a capacitive circuit only if potentials are changing, using a.c. or pulses for instance. A rather incomplete summary of capacitor usage might be:

It need not be a capacitor 'made for the job', of course, simply two conductors nearby and at different potentials.

(a) Removal of high-frequency a.c. potentials by 'decoupling', that is connecting a large capacitor between a circuit node and earth. This is mandatory in d.c. power supply circuits. Usually the capacitance need not be precisely known, as long as it is large, and leakage current is rarely a problem.

See Horowitz and Hill for detailed work on the use of capacitors, particularly, chapters 1, 4 and 6.

(b) Acting as a filtering component, in conjunction with resistors and/or inductors and/or amplifiers, in circuits which treat a.c. signals in ways which depend on their frequencies. In this case a capacitor needs to have a highly stable capacitance so that the filter, once set up, needs no adjustment. Leakage current should be small, but need not be treated as seriously as in usage(c).

Usage (a) is, of course, a filtering application also, but precision is not involved.

(c) Timing circuits. Because of Eqn(5.10), circuits can be designed in which capacitors control the rate of change of potentials and thus can be used for timing. Accuracy and low leakage currents are required.

(d) Sampling circuits. Potentials and charges need 'storing' for a time in some applications and a capacitor is clearly the obvious component to use. The leakage current must be low, but the capacitance need not be known accurately; however it must not change during the period the charge is stored.

Design procedure

A capacitor is a pair of plates separated by an insulating material. Eqn(4.5) shows that the larger the plate area A or relative permittivity ϵ_r and the smaller the gap x, the higher the capacitance C.

As space is usually at a premium in electronic equipment, components are designed to be as small as possible for a given function. For a capacitor, this means making x small as then A need not be too large. ϵ_r should also be large, but the material chosen sets up a constraint on x. For a capacitor to work up to a certain maximum potential V_m, the dielectric strength E_m of its insulator must be greater than V_m/x. There is little point in choosing a material of large ϵ_r if its dielectric strength is so low that x has to be made large to avoid avalanche breakdown. Moreover, for many applications a dielectric must be chosen whose insulation

The equation is for a parallel-plate, of course, but most real capacitors have a very large area and very small gap, so they behave virtually as a parallel-plate system even if the plates have been folded or rolled.

qualities are good, in other words it must have a very high resistivity.

The simplest way to see this compromise is to look at the energy stored when the capacitor is charged to its required maximum potential. Eqn(5.9) shows that the energy stored per unit volume of dielectric W_v is given by

$$W_v = \epsilon_0 \epsilon_r E^2 / 2$$

If size were the only criterion, therefore, a material with a high product of ϵ_r and E_m would be chosen.

For low leakage, on the other hand, it can be shown that the leakage current I_m at maximum applied potential V_m is proportional to E_m / ρ, so a large ratio ρ / E_m will be required if leakage is at a premium.

Exercise 5.2 Calculate the plate area and gap required for an optimum capacitor using polystyrene as the dielectric. The capacitance is to be 0.001 μF and the maximum working d.c. voltage 160 V. Show that the resulting capacitor has an insulation resistance greater than $10^{13} \Omega$.

(Polystyrene has the properties (worst case): relative permittivity 2.5, dielectric strength 20 kV mm^{-1}, resistivity 10^{15} Ωm.)

(Answer: Area = 360 mm^2; gap = 8 μm; resistance = 2.2 $\times$ $10^{13} \Omega$)

The answer to Exercise 5.2 should make it clear that even though the calculation using the parallel-plate formula is reasonable, a real capacitor could not be made that shape because the gap is so small and the area so large. Practical capacitors take the basic parallel-plate and either interleave, fold or roll it so as to occupy a volume of more convenient shape. The diagrams of capacitor structure below should make this clear.

Loveday, chapter 3, gives more detail of capacitor construction.

Non-polarized capacitors

This type of capacitor uses a film of plastic such as polystyrene, polyester or polycarbonate, alternatively a natural material like mica, as the dielectric. For very small values (up to a few tens of picofarads) the parallel-plate structure is used as such, and this is certainly the case for capacitors which are part of integrated circuits, but the metal foil and plastic sandwich is interleaved, rolled or folded for larger values. Figure 5.9(a) shows the structure of a non-polarized capacitor.

This term does *not* mean that there is no polarization; far from it — that is how any dielectric works! It simply shows that you can operate the capacitor with the p.d. across it in either direction, which is not the case with the 'polarized' type.

Polarized capacitors

For very large energy densities, the non-polar dielectrics mentioned above are less economical for space than are electrolytically formed aluminium and tantalum oxides. Electrolytic capacitors use as dielectric a layer of aluminium oxide formed on one foil and separated from the other foil by electrolyte. As the electrolyte conducts, the dielectric is just the oxide and is a very thin layer indeed so the capacitance will be large. E_m for the oxide is a high value and so the energy density is large also. Because the oxide layer was deposited when the component was manufactured the capacitor terminals must only be connected to the same polarities as were used in the forming process, or the oxide would lift off and allow a short-circuit to develop through the electrolyte. Hence the term 'polarized capacitors' for this type. Figure 5.9(b) shows the structure of an aluminium layer electrolytic capacitor and a solid tantalum type, which uses the same principle but metal particles rather than foil.

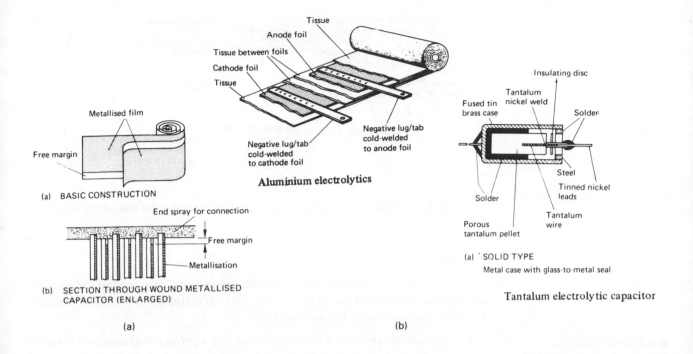

(a)

Metallised film

Free margin

(a) BASIC CONSTRUCTION

End spray for connection

Free margin

Metallisation

(b) SECTION THROUGH WOUND METALLISED
CAPACITOR (ENLARGED)

Tissue

Anode foil

Tissue between foils

Cathode foil

Tissue

Negative lug/tab
cold-welded
to cathode foil

Negative lug/tab
cold-welded
to anode foil

Aluminium electrolytics

(b)

Insulating disc

Tantalum
nickel weld

Fused tin
brass case

Solder

Steel

Tinned nickel
leads

Solder

Tantalum
wire

Porous
tantalum pellet

(a) SOLID TYPE
Metal case with glass-to-metal seal

Tantalum electrolytic capacitor

Fig. 5.9   Structure of some capacitors. From Loveday, courtesy Pitman Publishing Ltd, London.

Further Applications

For these, only a few notes will be given, pointing up features that illustrate the theoretical work carried out in this and earlier chapters. References will show where more detail can be found.

Dust precipitation

Many industrial processes produce waste gases and smoke in large quantities. The solid particles making up the smoke must be removed before release to the atmosphere, to avoid a serious pollution problem.

Luckily, at some point in most processes the smoke is above the boiling point of water and so is effectively dry. Electrostatic processes can be used without fear of charge leakage through any moisture, therefore.

The smoke passes up a chimney containing a thin wire held at a high negative potential relative to the chimney walls. The field close to the wire is greater than the dielectric strength of air, so ionization occurs there, generating quantities of electrons and positive ions which move out to the walls and back to the wire, respectively. On their journey out, the electrons readily attach themselves to dust particles, carrying them to the walls also, to which they stick and can then be removed mechanically. The chimney must be long enough, and the gas flow slow enough, to allow even the slowest-moving particle to reach the wall. Figure 5.10 shows the principle.

These techniques will only remove solid particles. They will not prevent the release of toxic gases, such as sulphur dioxide.

Avalanche conduction does not occur over the whole chimney width because the field is relatively low near the walls. This effect, of localized avalanche ionization producing ions which can then drift elsewhere, is called a *corona discharge*. The central wire is − rather than + because electrons, being lighter, are much more mobile than + ions.

For further details see Bolton, chapter 4.

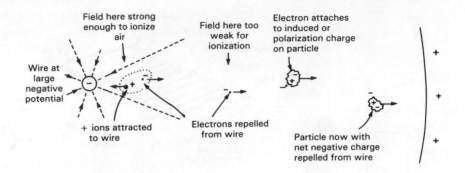

Fig. 5.10 Corona discharge as used in dust precipitation and xerography.

Xerography

The recent explosion in what is usually called photocopying is in large measure due to the xerographic process shown in Fig. 5.11. A metal drum, with a thin photo-resistive coating rotates in sequence past:

See marginal note above regarding a corona discharge.

Only a thin line of image strikes the drum at any point, so no blurring occurs.

(a) a positively charged wire, which produces a corona discharge and transfers positive ions on to the coating which, being in the dark, is an insulator at this point. So the surface retains a positive charge;

(b) a projected image of the master being copied. Where light falls, the coating conducts, electrons flowing through it to neutralize the positive charge;

(c) a spray of black dust ('toner') which has become charged by friction. Negatively charged toner particles stick to the parts of the coating not exposed to light, in the dark parts of the image in stage (b). Unused toner particles are collected and recycled;

(d) a sheet of paper to receive the copy. This is on a positively charged plate, so

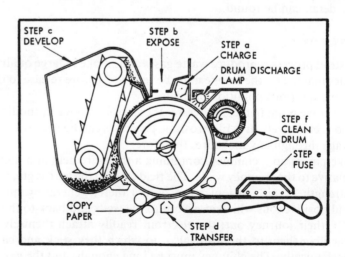

Fig. 5.11 The xerographic process (courtesy Rank-Xerox Ltd, Welwyn Garden City, Herts).

the negatively charged toner particles are pulled off and stick, thus copying the dark parts of the image as black on the paper;

(e) a brush to remove unused toner and ultraviolet light to neutralize the coating surface ready for stage(a);

(f) the sheet of paper passes under a heater which causes the toner particles to adhere fully into a permanent image.

For further details see *Nuffield Revised A Level Physics Students' Guide*, Unit E, or apply to Rank-Xerox Ltd, Welwyn Garden City, Herts.

Electrostatic microphones

If an air capacitor with a moveable plate is set up, the effect of moving the plate will depend on whether potential or charge is allowed to remain constant. If potential, charge will flow during the motion but the current will be proportional to the instantaneous value of the capacitance. If the plate moves closer, for instance, the capacitance will increase, so a further identical motion of the plate will cause a larger current flow. The system would thus be non-linear and therefore unsuitable as an audio microphone, for the reasons explained above under 'electrostatic loudspeakers'.

If, on the other hand, charge is kept constant, motion of the plate will not effect D, which depends only on the conduction charges. Thus E is also unaffected, and the potential will be proportional to the plate separation, from Eqn(3.9). This would be a linear system, therefore.

As long as the plates are very close together, and are of opposite polarity, external earths have little effect.

Figure 5.3 showed a capacitor microphone based on this principle, using an electret film as the moving charged plate.

Liquid crystal displays

The familiar display on most electronic watches and calculators is our final application of electrostatics. Certain materials have been discovered that, though normally transparent liquids, contain molecules that line up in a pattern in the presence of an electric field, rendering the material opaque. By designing a suitable arrangement of electrodes, a display system can be made that can generate any desired pattern, changeable by altering the electrode potentials. Figure 5.12 shows such a display system, which because fields and not currents are generated takes very little power from a supply.

Chapter 11 gives further details of the working of liquid crystals.

For further details see Wilson and Hawkes.

Summary

In the presence of a dielectric material (insulator) the ratio D/E and capacitance are both increased.

When an electric field is applied to a dielectric, the material is polarized and non-removeable charges appear on the surface. The value of D depends only on the conduction charges and geometry, but the potential gradient across the material is reduced because of the polarization.

These effects can be described by:

(a) a relative permittivity ϵ_r, representing the increase in ratio D/E;

(b) a polarization vector P which represents the polarization field acting against the applied field, and is given by $D = \epsilon_0 E + P$

In piezoelectric materials P can be induced by strain, and stress can generate P. In electrets P can be fixed in permanently.

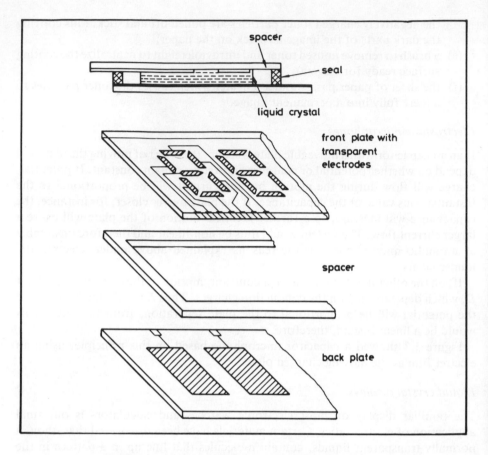

spacer

seal

liquid crystal

front plate with transparent electrodes

spacer

back plate

Fig. 5.12 Exploded view of a typical liquid-crystal display cell (courtesy G.F. Weston and the IEE; first published in *Electronics and Power*, April 1982).

The dielectric strength, E_m of an insulator is the potential gradient required to cause breakdown.

The field at the surface of a conductor increases with its curvature. For a spherical conductor the potential falls off as an inverse unity law. For a dipole, the field falls off according to an inverse cube.

A charged capacitor has potential energy $QV/2$. In becoming charged from a constant potential source the latter loses energy QV, so a net loss of $QV/2$ occurs.

Energy density within an electric field is given by $\epsilon_0 \epsilon_r E^2/2$.

For a small charge Q within a field E, force $F = QE$. If motion of the charge affects the field, F must be calculated from $F = -\,dW/dx$.

Electrostatic loudspeakers must use force on a constant charge, for linearity. Capacitor microphones must work at constant charge, for the same reason.

Dielectrics for capacitor use should have a high product $\epsilon_r E_m^2$ and a high value of ρ.

Dust precipitators and xerography use an electrical discharge to generate ions and transfer charge across a gap.

Liquid crystal systems use fields to produce a low power display.

Problems

*Indicates more challenging problems

Take ϵ_0 as $8.85 \times 10^{-12}\,\text{F m}^{-1}$ and 1 electron-charge as $-1.6 \times 10^{-19}\,\text{C}$.

5.1 A lightning flash lasts 75 μs. Assume, as a rough estimate, that the average current is 15 kA and that the flash occurs when the electric field strength between the cloud base, 0.6 km up, and the earth is 3000 kV m^{-1}
   (a) Calculate the p.d. between cloud and earth when the flash occurs.
   (b) Calculate the electrostatic energy released in the flash, assuming that the p.d. after the flash is near to zero.
   (c) Calculate the average power in the flash.

5.2 An air capacitor of plate area 0.002 m^2 and separation 0.08 mm is connected to a p.d. of 180 V. Calculate:
   (a) the electric flux density;
   (b) the force between the plates.

*5.3 A coaxial cable is required to have a high voltage on its inner conductor, the outer one being earthed.
   (a) What must the ratio of conductor diameters be to ensure maximum voltage for a given insulator?
   (b) What is the maximum voltage that could be used for buried coaxial power lines therefore, using polythene (dielectric strength 28000 kV m^{-1}) for an outer diameter of 0.2 m?

*5.4 Consider the electrostatic loudspeaker design in Fig. 5.13. It is proposed to make the diaphragm D maintain a constant potential of $+200$ V d.c., with no series resistor.

This problem might seem more logically solved by showing that the deflection in part (f) is not 0.5 mm if the support is linear; however, you have to solve a cubic in this case!

   At one position in use, A has a potential of $+100$ V. The resultant force causes the diaphragm to move 1 mm nearer B.

   Calculate, for this condition:
   (a) the capacitance of D to earth;
   (b) the capacitance of D to A;
   (c) the charge on D to maintain a potential of $+200$ V;
   (d) the force on D;
   (e) the elastic constant of D's support, in N m^{-1}.
   (f) If the system were linear, $+50$ V on A should produce a deflection of 0.5 mm. Carry out the calculation as above, to see whether the same elastic constant is required. If not, the system is non-linear.

5.5 Determine the force between two protons in a helium nucleus separated by a distance of 10^{-14} m. The proton has the same charge as the electron, but positive, and can be considered as a point charge.

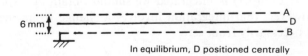

6 mm

In equilibrium, D positioned centrally

Fig. 5.13   Electrostatic loudspeaker design for Problem 5.4.

6 Magnetic Flux and Circuits

Objectives

☐ To make clear the experimental basis of electromagnetic induction and magnetic flux and to introduce magnetic materials.
☐ To relate flux with the current causing it and with the e.m.f. it can induce.
☐ To define a magnetic circuit and to derive equations for a general circuit and also for a simple one where flux lines are confined by material.
☐ To discuss the effects of gaps in a simple magnetic circuit.

Electromagnetic Induction

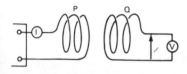

The experimental basis of this chapter is illustrated by the figure of two coils in the margin. A current I flows through coil P from a power supply, and any e.m.f. $\mathcal{E}$ generated by coil Q is measured by a high-resistance voltmeter.

By experiment, an e.m.f. can be detected under the following circumstances:

(a) the current in P changes;
(b) relative motion occurs between P and Q with I constant but not zero;
(c) certain materials like iron, called magnetic materials, move in the vicinity of P and Q with I constant but not zero;
(d) magnetized materials, such as magnets, move in the vicinity of P and Q with I constant or zero.

Coil P is not essential for part (d), of course.

These results also define magnetic materials and magnetization, which will be examined fully in Chapter 8.

The intuitive model used to describe this behaviour is that coil P and also magnetized material generate **magnetic flux** and that an e.m.f. is generated in coil Q when the flux passing through it changes. This generation of an e.m.f. by changing magnetic flux is called **electromagnetic induction**. A region where magnetic flux can be detected is called a **magnetic field**.

It is found in all the cases above that if the changes causing the e.m.f. are made more rapidly, the resulting e.m.f. is larger. The e.m.f. is also proportional to the number of turns on Q, all other things being equal. It would seem sensible, therefore, to define magnetic flux Φ (phi) such that the induced e.m.f. per turn $\mathcal{E}$ is equal to its rate of change. This is Faraday's law, which is most simply expressed as:

It should be understood that this direct equality is an invention. It could have been a square law, for example, which would have been just as valid, but later equations would have ended up much more complicated. Later we will write this equation in terms of electric field E rather than e.m.f. $\mathcal{E}$.

$$\mathcal{E} = -N\mathrm{d}\Phi/\mathrm{d}t \tag{6.1}$$

Defining a quantity by its own rate of change does not always make for easy understanding. If Eqn(6.1) is integrated we should obtain an expression for Φ itself. Note, however, that integration involves a change from one value Φ_1 to another Φ_2, not necessarily from zero:

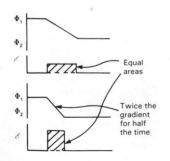

$$\int \mathcal{E}\,\mathrm{d}t = -N \int_{\Phi_1}^{\Phi_2} \mathrm{d}\Phi = -N(\Phi_2 - \Phi_1) \tag{6.2}$$

If the flux through a coil is changed over a period, and the instantaneous values of $\mathscr{E}$ are plotted against time, the flux change must be the area under this graph. For the same change, the area will be equal whether produced as a large $\mathscr{E}$ for a short time or a smaller value over a longer period.

Eqn(6.2) gives the unit of Φ as the volt-second/turn, which is also known as the **weber** (Wb).

W. Weber (1804 – 1891) devised the first system of electrical units.

Magnetic flux and current

If sinusoidal a.c. in coil P is used to generate the flux, the e.m.f. in coil Q is found to be cosinusoidal, as long as only linear magnetic materials such as air are present, and its peak value is proportional to the frequency of the a.c. This suggests that at least in the presence of air, the flux is proportional to the current in coil P. In that case, the equation for the variation of flux through Q with time must be $\Phi = \Phi_0 \sin \omega t$, where Φ_0 is the peak value and ω the angular frequency. Faraday's Law applied to this gives:

Yorke, chapter 3, gives details of the equations of alternating waveforms.

$$\mathscr{E} = -N\mathrm{d}(\Phi_0 \sin\omega t)\mathrm{d}t$$
$$= -N\omega\Phi_0 \cos\omega t$$

which is a cosinusoid whose peak value is $N\omega\Phi_0$.

Flux lines and flux conservation

If a small coil is placed in a magnetic field, then removed to a region where it is presumed there is no field, the flux through the coil while it was in the field can be obtained by finding $\int\mathscr{E}\,\mathrm{d}t/N$ during the removal. It is found that the answer obtained depends on the orientation of the coil. One particular direction, and 180° from it, give a maximum response. The direction of the coil axis for these cases defines the **direction of a flux line**, as Fig. 6.1 shows.

In an alternating field, the coil axis lines up along a flux line for maximum a.c. response in a similar way.

This could be done by measuring charge Q passed in a circuit of known resistance R as $Q = \int I\mathrm{d}t = \int V\mathrm{d}t/R$.

A compass placed in a field points along lines exactly matching the flux lines just defined, so our picture is consistent with other starting points in magnetism.

Note that a coil responds to the total flux through it, regardless of which direction any flux lines travel. What we are doing here is to maximise the amount of changing flux the coil 'sees'. Later we can define the direction of an arrow drawn along a flux line.

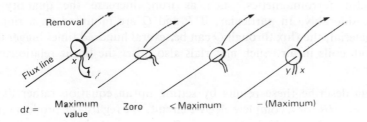

Fig. 6.1   Orientation of a test coil showing flux line direction.

Finally, in this first look at flux, consider a box made up of search coils as in Fig. 6.2.

If an alternating magnetic field is generated in the space surrounded by the coils, an alternating induced e.m.f. can be detected in each coil, whose amplitude will be proportional to the flux through that particular coil. If two coils are connected in series, the response is proportional to the total flux through them. If all the coils are connected in series with the same orientation relative to the centre of the box the

In practice some flux escapes between the wires and is unaccounted for.

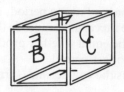

Fig. 6.2   Coils surrounding a space.

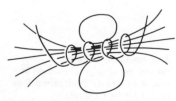

Orientation of letters fits Fig. 6.2.

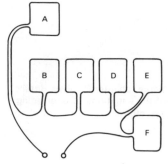

Coil and flux loops generated by it. The flux lines will be given a direction in Chapter 7. See any elementary Physics book for an account of the use of iron filings to show flux patterns.

total response, which is the total flux emerging from the box, is reduced to a very low value and, under ideal conditions, would presumably be zero. This applies whether magnetic materials are present or not, and whether the generator of flux is inside, outside or even within a wall of the box. The experiment illustrates an important property:

Magnetic flux is conserved under all conditions

On diagrams showing magnetic flux, this is made clear by drawing the flux as continuous loops, passing through flux generators and into the space outside them. The flux patterns can be found tediously, by coil response methods, or quickly by using the tendency of iron filings to cluster along flux lines.

Magnetomotive Force, Flux and Reluctance

Experiments, using coils like P and Q earlier in the chapter, show that:

(a) In the absence of magnetic materials, flux is proportional to the current and the number of turns in P.

(b) Magnetic materials alter the amount of flux produced. Certain materials called ferromagnetics, such as iron, increase the quantity of flux considerably. In particular, if P and Q are mounted on a ring of such material, the flux through Q can be several hundred times bigger than with both coils in air. Such materials also upset the linear relationship in (a) above.

We can describe these results by setting up an equation rather like Ohm's equation $\mathscr{E} = IR$ for a complete electric circuit. We regard the product (current × number of turns) as equivalent to e.m.f., flux as equivalent to current, and invent a quantity **reluctance** S to express the relationship between them, like resistance in electric circuits. To make the analogy even more obvious, (current × number of turns) is called **magnetomotive force** (m.m.f.) $\mathscr{M}$, so a magnetic circuit equation can be defined as:

$$\mathscr{M} = \Phi S \tag{6.3}$$

Continuing the analogy, we say that the m.m.f. generates flux loops, which 'flow' round a magnetic circuit. The number of loops, that is the total flux, is controlled by the reluctance of the magnetic circuit.

Reluctance can be measured directly from determinations of $\mathscr{M}$ and Φ or, as we shall see in Chapter 8, from measurements of self and mutual inductance.

Magnetic Circuits

Simple circuits

The magnetic circuit associated with a coil in air, like P above, fills the whole of space, and we cannot say much about it yet. If, on the other hand, a low reluctance ferromagnetic ring is used, and coils P and Q are both wound on it, much more flux is generated by P, of which virtually none escapes into the air around the ring. Therefore we have a closely defined magnetic circuit. Nearly all the flux loops in such a circuit are contained within the material.

If experiments are performed on rings of different dimensions, the reluctance to flux generated in coils wrapped round them is found to be proportional to the average circumference l of the ring and inversely proportional to the area A 'seen' by the flux. The proportionality constant is made up in a similar way to the connection between D and E in electrostatics, by a universal constant and by a multiplier which depends on the material:

For a simple magnetic circuit with parallel flux lines and no gaps:

$$S = \frac{l}{\mu_0 \mu_r A} \tag{6.4}$$

where μ_0 is called the **magnetic constant** and is given the value $4\pi \times 10^{-7}$ while μ_r is called the **relative permeability** of the magnetic material making up the ring.

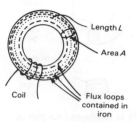

Length L

Area A

Coil

Flux loops contained in iron

The unit of μ_0 is the henry m^{-1}, as explained in Chapter 8. μ_0 is defined because it follows from the definition of the ampere in Chapter 9, whereas ϵ_0 is an experimental result.

An iron ring of magnetic length (average circumference) 0.2 m and magnetic area of cross-section 400 mm² has two coils wound round it, P with 100 turns and Q with 400. When the current through P increases at a rate of 2 mA/ms, a steady e.m.f. of 0.4 V is induced is in Q. Find the relative permeability of the iron under these conditions.

Worked Example 6.1

Solution: Eqn(6.3) relates flux to current. As a rate of change of current is involved, we shall need to differentiate the equation. Variations in both S and $\mathcal{M}$ will have their effect on Φ, so in this case S is assumed constant with Φ, though this would in fact be only approximately the case. The value of μ_r obtained will be a slope value, therefore, applying only under the conditions described. Using the usual symbols, with N_1 for primary turns, coil P, and N_2 for secondary, coil Q, and ignoring the minus sign in Faraday's Equation:

Note the similarity to slope capacitance in Chapter 5.

$$\mathcal{M} = S\Phi$$
$$\mathrm{d}(\mathcal{M})/\mathrm{d}t = S\,\mathrm{d}\Phi/\mathrm{d}t = S\mathcal{E}/N_2$$

As N_1 is constant, $N_1\mathrm{d}I/\mathrm{d}t = S\mathcal{E}/N_2$

$$= l\mathcal{E}/N_2\mu_0\mu_r A$$

Rearranging:
$$\mu_r = l\mathcal{E}/N_2\mu_0 A N_1(\mathrm{d}I/\mathrm{d}t)$$

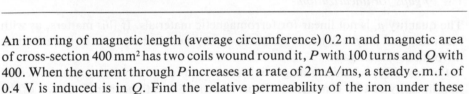

$$= \frac{0.2 \times 0.4}{400 \times 4\pi \times 10^{-7} \times 400 \times 10^{-6} \times 100 \times 2}$$
$$= 1990$$

Effect of narrow gaps

The answer to Worked Example 6.1 shows that the relative permeability of a material like iron is very high. Magnetic circuits of low reluctance can be made, therefore, but only so long as the whole circuit is made up of such a material. If even a small air gap exists in a ring, its effect will be out of all proportion to its size. If a ring of iron of $\mu_r = 2000$ has an air gap making up 1/2000 of its magnetic length, for instance 1 mm in 2 m, the reluctance will be double that of a complete iron ring. If the gap were 10 mm, the high permeability of the iron would simply make it a low reluctance path from one side of the gap to the other; the gap provides most of the reluctance. This is especially important in rotating machinery like motors and generators, where clearances must exist between fixed and rotating parts, and in transformers, where to allow windings to be fitted the core must be in two parts that butt together.

When the gap is not 'small' relative to the cross-section of the circuit, the flux lines bow out in a way very similar to the electric field lines in Fig. 3.9(b). For situations where the gap is narrow enough for the flux lines across it to be deemed parallel, Eqn(6.4) can be applied to both ring material and air, considering the reluctances to be in series and using the same area A for both. Thus if the ring length is l, the gap width w and other symbols are as before and again for parallel flux:

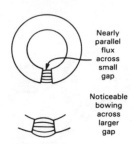

Nearly parallel flux across small gap

Noticeable bowing across larger gap

This is explained further in Chapter 9.

Adding 'difficulties', as with resistances in series.

$$ S = \frac{l}{\mu_0 \mu_r A} + \frac{w}{\mu_0 A} \tag{6.5} $$

Use of gaps for linearization

The quantity μ_r is not linear for ferromagnetic materials. If this matters, as with recording and playback heads for audio work, the reluctance can be linearized by introducing an air gap.

For instance, consider a magnetic circuit required to have a maximum overall non-linearity of 1%. If material of non-linearity 5% is to be used, only 1/5 of the circuit should be made of this material, the remainder being an air gap, which is perfectly linear. The price paid is a five-fold increase in reluctance compared with using the material with no gap, so more m.m.f. will be needed to provide a given flux.

If a system has a non-linear response e.g.:

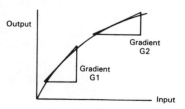

Output

Gradient G2

Gradient G1

Input

The percentage non-linearity can be defined as:
$$ \frac{G_2 - G_1}{\text{average } (G_1, G_2)} \times 100 $$

Non-linearities in μ_r are considered in Chapter 8.

Summary

Magnetic flux Φ is generated by electric currents and by magnetized materials and is detected by the e.m.f. $\mathscr{E}$ induced within a coil through which it passes. If the coil has N turns:

$$ \mathscr{E} = -N\mathrm{d}\Phi/\mathrm{d}t $$

If the flux changes from Φ_1 to Φ_2:

$$ N(\Phi_1 - \Phi_2) = -\int\mathscr{E}\,\mathrm{d}t $$

The output of a coil through which sinusoidal a.c. flux passes is a cosinusoid of amplitude proportional to the frequency and amplitude of the changing flux.

The direction of a flux line is the direction of the axis of a small detecting coil when its response is a maximum.

Magnetic flux is conserved under all circumstances so must be drawn as continuous loops.

Within a magnetic circuit, flux Φ and magnetomotive force $\mathcal{M}$, equal to (number of turns × current) of magnetizing coil, are related by $\mathcal{M} = S\Phi$ where S is the reluctance of the circuit.

For simple magnetic circuits, with parallel flux lines, of length l and cross-sectional area A, $S = l/\mu_0\mu_r A$, where μ_0 is the magnetic constant and μ_r is the relative permeability of the circuit material.

If a magnetic circuit is broken by gaps small enough that the flux lines can be assumed parallel across them, the total reluctance is given by adding the gap reluctances to that of the rest of the circuit.

Problems

*Indicates a more challenging problem.

$\mu_0 = 4\pi \times 10^{-7}\,\text{H m}^{-1}$.

6.1 A spark-ignition system in a car consists of a transformer, whose low voltage winding is of 160 turns on an iron core of relative permeability 3000. The effective length of iron in the magnetic circuit is 75 mm and its cross-sectional area 100 mm^2. The spark plug, under compression, needs 12 kV to operate it, and the contact breaker in series with the low voltage winding reduces a current of 2.5 A to zero in 1.2 ms. Calculate

(a) the core reluctance;
(b) the rate of change of flux in the core;
(c) the number of turns required for the high-voltage winding.

*6.2 Figure 6.3 shows a system for detecting contact between a rapidly moving safety door and its frame, for operation in a hostile environment where switches would be unreliable.

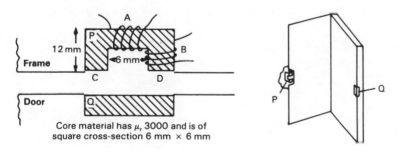

Fig. 6.3 Electromagnetic door sensor for Problem 6.2.

Coil A has 180 turns and 20 mA flows through it; coil B has 1000 turns. In all cases assume the magnetic length is the length of the line joining the centres of all the cross-sectional areas.

(a) When the door is wide open, assume the path to flux of the air between faces C and D has the same reluctance as a rectangular tube of air 6 mm × 6 mm cross-section and 10 mm long. Calculate the reluctance of the U-core and this air path.

This is a very rough estimate, but as the flux is so low with the door open anyway, it does not matter too much what reluctance value is taken. You might like to halve the reluctance of the open-door air path and see what difference it makes to the answers.

This e.m.f. could perhaps be used to activate a latching system for the door.

(b) Calculate the reluctance of the magnetic circuit when the door is closed, if a 0.04 mm gap then exists at each end of the U-core (assume flux parallel in this gap).

(c) Estimate the charge passed round the circuit containing coil B when the door closes from fully open, if the total circuit resistance is 20 Ω.

(d) Estimate the average e.m.f. generated in coil B during the last 0.1 mm of closure if the door closes at 0.5 m s^{-1}.

Magnetic Vectors

7

□ To introduce a magnetic vector B defined from the force on a current and to relate it to magnetic flux.

□ To extend the force on a current so it applies to a moving charged particle, and to show how this predicts both motor and dynamo effects.

□ To find general rules for determining field and induced current directions.

□ To make a general equation connecting changing flux with induced e.m.f. and to introduce the concept of a non-conservative field.

□ To introduce a new vector H equal to the magnetic scalar potential gradient, and show its uses.

□ To derive an equation connecting a current with the integrated field round it and apply the equation.

□ To find the field produced by a tiny element of current.

Vector B and Flux

So far, magnetism has made its presence felt only by the induction of an e.m.f. in a coil when the magnetic flux through it changes. Electrons in the wire must feel a force under these conditions, to enable them to move and drive a current if the coil circuit is complete.

Force produced by a magnetic field can be detected in other situations, however, when whole objects rather than just the electrons in them can feel a force. Experiments can be carried out where magnetic materials such as iron, or wires conducting currents, respond to a magnetic field and the strength of this field can be related to the forces produced.

We shall see that B is the same as magnetic flux density, but will be defined from force on a current and referred to as 'B field'. It is sometimes called **magnetic induction** also.

Unfortunately the term 'magnetic field strength' is applied by different authors to both B and H, so it will not be used in this book for either!

B from force on a current

By measuring the force on a straight wire, carrying a current through the magnetic field of a small gap within a magnetic circuit, the following results are obtained, illustrated in Fig. 7.1:

(a) As long as the wire is well into the gap, the force does not depend on its exact position, suggesting that such a gap does represent a region of uniform field.

(b) The force F on the wire is proportional to the length l of wire exposed to the field, the current I in the wire and the sine of the angle θ between the wire and the presumed field direction directly across the gap.

(c) The direction of F is at right angles to a plane containing the wire and the field direction.

This is called the motor effect, from its obvious application. Result (b) is summarized by an equation which allows us to define a quantity B:

$$F = BIl \sin \theta \qquad (7.1)$$

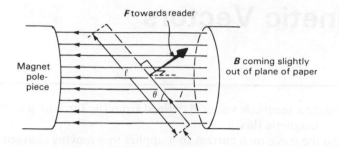

Fig. 7.1   Current-carrying wire in a uniform magnetic field.

This however only predicts the magnitude of the force, not the direction described in part (c) above. To write an equation containing all the information, a shorthand form called the **vector** or **cross product of vectors** is used:

$$F = I(l \times B) \tag{7.2}$$

This means 'F is a vector of magnitude $BIl \sin \theta$, and direction at right angles to the plane containing l and B, and such that if a right-hand screw thread rotates from l to B, F is along the direction of progress of the screw'.

The units of B are most easily seen by writing down the equation that applies when l and B are at right angles so $\sin \theta = 1$. Making B the subject gives $B = F/Il$, so B has the unit of $N\,A^{-1}m^{-1}$, which is also called the **tesla** (T).

Equivalence of B and flux density

Already, it should seem intuitively obvious that B is connected with the density or closeness of magnetic flux lines. Where flux lines are uniform, across a small gap in a magnetic circuit, B is constant, whereas in situations where flux is non-uniform, such as near a bar magnet, B is larger where the flux lines are closer, near the end or 'pole' of the magnet. To make formal the connection between B and Φ, we need to set up a rather artificial experiment in which we discuss the energy transfers involved when a wire is allowed to move in a field.

Figure 7.2 shows a U-shaped circuit, containing a battery of e.m.f. $\mathscr{E}$, and is completed by a light, straight wire PQ, which can slide with no friction along as shown, in a magnetic field of strength B. The battery, wires and contacts have zero resistance. It may be thought that as soon as the loose wire is dropped on, an infinite current would flow, as the resistance is zero. However, once a current I

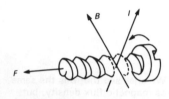

N. Tesla (1856 – 1943) invented the a.c. induction motor. We shall shortly find that the Wb m^{-2} is also a correct unit, but this has not yet been proved in this development of the subject.

The zero resistance and zero friction are needed not to make the system work but to simplify the calculations and make the energy transfer obvious. A real system would work, but energy lost as heat would complicate things.

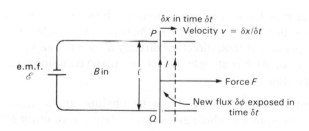

Fig. 7.2   Equivalence of flux density and B-field.

starts to flow, the loose wire feels a force and begins to move out. In doing so, it is increasing the flux passing through the whole circuit. The rate of increase of this flux depends on the speed of the wire, and the wire cannot travel faster than a speed where the rate of flux increase generates an e.m.f. equal and opposite to that of the battery, $\mathscr{E}$. Speed v is limited, therefore, and so is current I, as once the two e.m.f.s balance, I cannot increase any further. We will set up an equation based on the energy transfer involved, and substitute to eliminate F and v and relate B, defined from force on a conductor, to Φ, defined from the e.m.f. induced when it changes.

All the power $\mathscr{E}I$ taken from the battery is being transferred into mechancial power given by Fv, as there is no other sink of energy, so

$$\mathscr{E}I = Fv$$

Using Eqns (6.1) and (7.2), noting that $N = 1$ and using δ quantities to allow cancellation:

$$I\delta\Phi/\delta t = BIlv = BIl\delta x/\delta t$$

I and δt cancel, leaving:

$$\delta\Phi = Bl\delta x = B\delta A$$

where δA is the new area exposed to flux by the motion of the wire. We have achieved a connection between B and Φ. If a large area of uniform flux is considered, the δ operators can be dropped and the equation:

$$B = \Phi/A \tag{7.3}$$

produced. This indicates that the unit of B could be Wb m^{-2} and that B can be described as **magnetic flux density**.

For non-uniform flux we follow exactly the same arguments as those leading to the current conservation equation (2.18). Repeat the discussion from Eqn (2.13) to Eqn (2.18), substituting magnetic flux density B for current density J and magnetic flux Φ for current I. The example below Eqn (2.14) could now be the concentrated flux between the shaped polepieces of a typical strong magnet. Eqn (2.17) becomes

$$\Phi = \iint \mathbf{B}.\mathbf{d}A \tag{7.4}$$

and Eqn (2.18) becomes the equation expressing the conservation of flux, which the 'box of coils' experiment in Chapter 6 illustrated:

$$\oiint \mathbf{B}.\mathbf{d}A = 0 \tag{7.5}$$

A coil of 200 turns is wrapped round a toroid ('doughnut') of iron. The axial length of the toroid is 0.75 m and it is broken by a plane-sided gap of width 2 mm. When a current of 2 A passes through the coil, the iron has a μ_r of 2500. Determine the force on a wire carrying a current of 10 A through the gap at right angles to the field. The length of wire within the gap is 0.15 m. Ignore edge effects in the gap and flux leakage.

Solution: We need to find the total flux generated within the magnetic circuit, using Eqn (6.3) and Eqn (6.5), then find B using Eqn (7.4) and finally apply Eqn (7.2) to find the force.

Energy transfer = force × distance so energy transfer/second (power) = force × distance/second (velocity).

Some books *define* B as flux density, but this is no more fundamental than defining it from force on a current — remember it is all a circular argument! If you define B this way, you then have to argue the sliding wire 'experiment' from the other end to show that it leads to $F = BIl$.

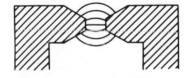

Flux across a powerful magnet gap

This is often differentiated in more advanced work and expressed as div $B = 0$, as in the similar case of div $D = \rho$ in Chapter 4.

Worked Example 7.1

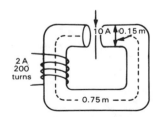

Ignoring the 2 mm compared with 0.75 m in 1. Don't worry about an unknown A appearing at this point. Unless the question is faulty, it should cancel later!

Using symbols as they appear in the equations: from Eqn(6.5), adding reluctances as they are in series:

$$S = \frac{1}{\mu_0 \mu_r A} + \frac{w}{\mu_0 A} = \frac{1}{\mu_0 A}\left(\frac{1}{\mu_r} + w\right)$$

$$= \frac{1}{4\pi \times 10^{-7} A}\left(\frac{0.75}{2500} + 0.002\right) = 1830/A$$

From Eqn(6.3): $\Phi = \mathcal{M}/S = 400A/1830 = 0.2186A$

From Eqn(7.4), as the flux is uniform and the area is at right angles to it:

$B = \Phi/A = 0.2186$ (A cancels)

From Eqn(7.2), as the wire is at right angles to the flux:

$F = BIl = 0.2186 \times 10 \times 0.15 = 0.328$ N

Force on a moving charged particle

As a charged particle in motion is equivalent to an electric current, it will feel a force, which it should be possible to calculate.

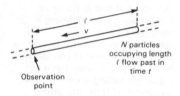

Consider particles of charge q flowing at speed v along a uniform tube. In time t a 'length' l of charge, containing N particles, flows past a fixed point; v is obviously equal to l/t.

Charge flowing in time $t = Nq$, so current I, that is the charge flowing past per second $= Nq/t$.

If the wire is at right angles to a magnetic field B, the force on length l of it will be $BIl = BNql/t = BNqv$, so this must also be the force on the N particles.

Force per particle therefore $= Bqv$.

By analogy with the force on a wire at an angle to the field, we can write a complete expression as

$$F = q(v \times B) \tag{7.6}$$

where the format is the same as in Eqn(7.2) and is explained below that equation.

As the force produced by a magnetic field on a moving charged particle is at right angles to its velocity:

(a) the particle speed does not change from this cause and;

(b) if there are no electric fields present the particle moves in a circular path or, if it has a component of velocity along the field, in a helix. This will be pursued further in Chapter 10.

Directional Rules and Lenz' Law

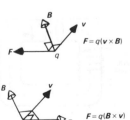

When the cross product of vectors was introduced, it was described in terms of the progress of a right-hand screw thread. This is purely convention, but the order of variables within the cross product brackets of Eqn(7.2) and Eqn(7.6) requires some justification; if the order is changed, the direction of F becomes the exact opposite. The correct direction can be determined by experiment, once conventions have been established for current and field directions. The usual conventions are:

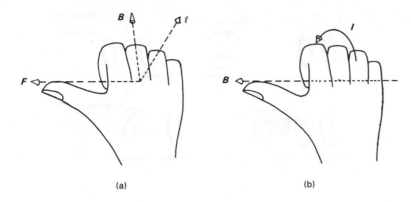

(a)   (b)

Fig. 7.3   The right-hand rule.

(a) Current direction is that of positive charge movement.
(b) Field direction is the direction a properly set up magnetic compass will point in the field.

If experiments are carried out, the terms in the equations are indeed found to be in the correct order.

Many rules have been devised to allow a quick determination of the directions of forces and fields in magnetism, and often confusion results, particularly when Fleming's rules are used, with one hand for motors and the other for dynamos. Fewer errors are made when only one rule is used, the **right hand rule**, which can be applied to all cases. If the right hand is held as in Fig. 7.3(a), a movement from finger roots to fingertips corresponds to a rotation that advances a right-hand screw thread in the direction of the thumb. Thus it can be immediately applied to Eqn(7.2) as shown, and the hand oriented to fit any problem.

However, the use of the right hand does not end here. Now the direction of B is defined, the current direction required in a coil setting up a field can be related to the resulting B direction. By experiment it is also found to fit the right-hand rule, as Fig. 7.3(b) shows.

The only use needed of the left hand is for the motion of negative particles such as electrons.

Finally, we look at the direction in which currents produced from induced e.m.f.s. flow.

Consider a flat coil surrounding a region in which magnetic flux is changing. By experiment, if B through the coil increases in the direction of observation, current flows anti-clockwise.

We will analyse this from two points of view, one to connect up what happens with energy considerations and produce a rule, the other to derive an important equation connecting E and B, which represents Faraday's law in a more general way.

Energy analysis — Lenz' law

In the coil referred to above, with the induced current counterclockwise in the plane of the page, the current must itself produce a field. By the right-hand rule,

It is arguable that the direction of B is defined so it fits diagram (a) above and not (b), rather than that equation (a) is right and (b) wrong. However, this is probably a discussion at the coffee-break level only! Self-consistency is the important principle here.

Compare with marginal figure below Eqn(7.2).

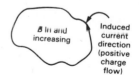

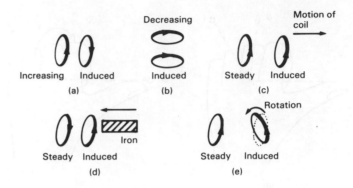

Fig. 7.4 Induced current directions for Exercise 7.1.

this field will be coming out of the page, acting against the increase of flux that caused the current in the first place. Similar experiments show that the invariable effect of a magnetic input to a system is to induce e.m.f.s which, if allowed to drive currents, will act against the input in an attempt to maintain the magnetic field as it was. This seems eminently reasonable, because if the opposite occurred, and the generated fields helped the input, the input would be effectively increased, so would the generated fields and so on, until an infinite field was produced from what could have been a tiny input! This would be against the Second Law of Thermodynamics, as mechanical energy cannot be created except from a heat flow between different temperatures, and certainly not in the spontaneous way just suggested. This tendency, in real life, for magnetic inputs always to produce effects that act against them, is referred to as **Lenz' law**. So the direction of an induced current can be determined by first deciding which way a magnetic field must be made to act against the one causing the current, then using the right-hand rule to find the current direction to produce that opposing field.

Exercise 7.1

Justify the directions of the induced currents in Fig. 7.4. The thick part of each coil represents the side nearest to the reader, as in a perspective drawing.

Though it could refer to the more distant side and still work!

Vector analysis and the non-conservative field

In Chapter 3, the flow of current in a circuit was related to the potential gradient, which was set up by a source of e.m.f. When magnetic flux changes through a coil, a current flows if the circuit is complete and an e.m.f. can be measured between the ends of the circuit if it is broken. However the e.m.f. in this case cannot be isolated and, more importantly, there is nowhere in the circuit where the measured potential gradient is in the opposite direction to current flow, as it is through a working battery. Figure 7.5 shows this distinction. If a closed path is followed round a circuit containing a magnetically induced e.m.f., a net p.d. will be found back at the starting point, equal in value to the e.m.f. In other words what drives electromagnetically induced current is a non-conservative field. $\oint E.dl$ is not zero.

It is perhaps like Escher's picture of an apparently upward staircase which nevertheless is a closed path, but don't take the analogy too far!

The loop integral must be equal to the induced e.m.f., in fact, which is itself equal to the rate of change of flux through the area surrounded by the loop. Using Eqn(7.4) we can relate this to B and the way it varies across this area, to produce an

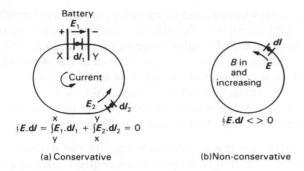

Fig. 7.5   Conservative and non-conservative fields.

equation that expresses Faraday's law in a particularly concise and useful way:

$$\oint E.dl = -\frac{d}{dt}\left(\oiint B.dA\right) \tag{7.7}$$

The negative sign expresses Lenz' law.

Eqn(7.7) makes no reference to conductors. It therefore predicts that within a region of changing magnetic flux, an E field exists in the form of loops, which can drive a current through any conductor placed there.

As an example, any conductor in an alternating magnetic field will respond with circulating currents within itself, called **Eddy currents**. These cause problems in transformers, but are used in induction motors, including linear motors.

Similarity of motor and dynamo effects

A charged particle launched into a magnetic field at right angles to the flux lines will follow a circular path. The direction of its orbit can be predicted by Lenz' law.

Figure 7.6 shows an electron moving in a magnetic field under three different conditions. B is into the page in all cases:

(a) The electron is free, and launched from the left-hand side. It moves in a circular path to counteract the applied field by producing a field out of the page. Being negative, the left hand has to be used, predicting an orbit as shown.

In more advanced work this is differentiated and written as curl $E = -\partial B/\partial t$. Carter, chapter 8, gives details.

Because if E drives a current, the field set up by that current (predictable from the right-hand rule) opposes the change in flux.

See, for example, Laithwaite, chapter 7.

A circular path is on the assumption that the field actually produced by the particle has negligible effect on the applied field. This is true for particles in electron streams, but not so for particles in conductors, whose path is therefore more complex. The general direction of travel applies nevertheless.

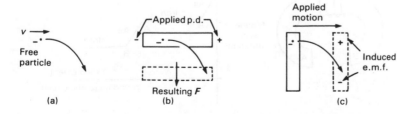

Fig. 7.6   Motor and dynamo effects from particle motion.

(b) The electron is within a conducting rod containing a potential gradient. This will cause it (and all the other electrons in the rod) to move to the right and thus follow a path of similar shape to (a). The whole rod will be forced down, therefore, and the result is described as the **motor effect**.

(c) The electron is within a rod moving from left to right across the field. Again the electron, along with all the others, follows a curved path, this time ending up nearer the bottom of the rod and thus setting up an induced e.m.f. across the rod. This is called the **dynamo effect**.

Thus the apparently opposite actions of motors and dynamos are seen to be results of the same alteration in the path of an electron crossing a magnetic field. This observation by itself does not help in carrying out calculations, but it is useful to bear in mind the common origin of the two effects. In Chapter 10 we shall meet another result of charged particle motion, the Hall effect, where the particle moves across a slab of material rather than a rod.

Magnetic Scalar Potential and Vector H

On many occasions B may be required at a point, perhaps to calculate the force on a wire or charged particle. If the magnetic circuit is simple, like those discussed in Chapter 6, B is simply given by Φ/A. For more complex circuits the concept of a magnetic scalar potential is useful.

Pursuing the analogy between electric and magnetic circuits a little further, we now ask whether there is any magnetic equivalent to potential difference in an electric circuit. There perhaps ought to be, as we have already have m.m.f. as a direct equivalent to e.m.f., the former 'driving' flux, the latter current.

Consider a magnetic circuit as in Fig. 7.7, with a driving coil and an air gap.

If point A is considered, quite arbitrarily, as the starting potential, then imagining flux 'moving' anti-clockwise it loses a little potential along the iron to B and much across the high reluctance of the air gap back to A. Unlike an electric circuit with a battery, but very like one exposed to changing magnetic flux, there is no region within the circuit where the potential gradient is positive. The flux is 'set in motion' by the m.m.f. and only losses in potential can be observed. There is no zero of potential, nor can an absolute 'potential' be quoted, only differences.

A potential described in this way is called **magnetic scalar potential**. It should be clear that it is an invention, to aid the understanding of magnetic circuits. We will

With no coil, the flux would vanish, unless a permanent magnet were made, in which case the situation would resemble an electric circuit with a battery. This will be discussed in Chapter 9.

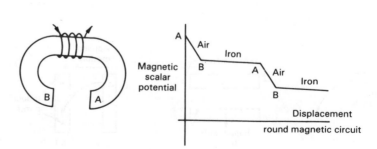

Fig. 7.7 Scalar potential in a magnetic circuit.

shortly find that the magnetic scalar potential gradient H is a particularly useful aspect of the idea.

Returning to the problem of finding B in a complex magnetic circuit, we can consider a very small part, where the flux lines are virtually parallel and the magnetic scalar potential will change at a uniform rate; B can be found from this as follows, using the figure in the margin.

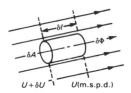

For the small cylinder, we can apply Eqn(6.3) using magnetic scalar potential difference (m.s.p.d.) U instead of m.m.f., by analogy with the use of p.d. rather than e.m.f., for a small region of an electric circuit.

If S is the reluctance of the small cylinder:

$$\delta U = \delta \Phi \, S$$
$$\text{so} \quad B = \delta \Phi / \delta A = \delta U / S \delta A$$
$$= \delta U \mu_0 \mu_r \delta A / \delta l \delta A \quad \text{using Eqn(6.4)}$$
$$= \mu_0 \mu_r \delta U / \delta l$$

At a point:

$$B = \mu_0 \mu_r \mathrm{d}U/\mathrm{d}l$$

As with D and E, it is possible to follow through magnetism by regarding magnetic scalar potential gradient as $B/\mu_0\mu_r$, but again are difficulties when non-linear and non-isotropic materials are met.

The magnetic vector H

Thus B at a point can be determined from the gradient of the magnetic scalar potential there. The latter therefore behaves in a mathematically similar way to potential gradient in a conductor, which causes a current flow according to $J = \sigma E$ (Eqn 3.6).

Because of this similarity, magnetic scalar potential gradient $\mathrm{d}U/\mathrm{d}l$ is regarded as an important vector in its own right, called H. So:

$$B = \mu_0 \mu_r H \tag{7.8}$$

By analogy with electric field and potential, we can show a finite change in magnetic scalar potential as:

$$U_2 - U_1 = \int H.\mathrm{d}l \tag{7.9}$$

This suggests that H is a conservative field but, as we shall see, in the presence of currents it is not. $\oint H.\mathrm{d}l$ is not the same for all paths, as will be clear shortly.

H is also called m.m.f. gradient, magnetizing force and magnetic field strength so the term 'H field' will be used here!

Compare with the development of the corresponding electrostatic line integral, up to Eqn(3.12).

Ampere's law

In a simple magnetic circuit, with parallel flux lines, B can be determined by combining Eqns(6.4) and (7.4), or by obtaining the H field from m.m.f./total magnetic circuit length, then using Eqn(7.8). Sometimes, however, only part of the magnetic circuit is involved.

From the data in Worked Example 7.1, determine the m.s.p.d. across the gap. This could be done by expressing the gap as an equivalent length of iron and comparing this with the total iron length through which the m.m.f. has to drive flux. Hence find H and thus B in the gap. (Answer: m.s.p.d. = 348 A; $H = 1.74 \times 10^5$ A m^{-1}; $B = 0.219$ T.)

To deal with more complex cases we need to find how the magnetic scalar potential varies within the circuit. One way of carrying this out experimentally is by using many search coils connected in series and mounted on a flexible tube, an arrangement called a Rogowski spiral.

Exercise 7.2

Rogowski spiral:

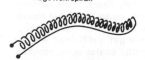

See also *Nuffield A Level Physics Teachers' Guide*, Original version, Unit 7.

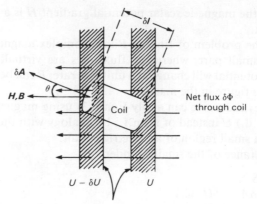

Magnetic scalar equipotential surfaces

Fig. 7.8   m.s.p.d. across a coil within magnetic flux.

Consider the response of a tiny search coil of small but finite length in a magnetic field, as shown in Fig. 7.8.

We will show now that the flux through the coil is proportional to the m.s.p.d. between its ends, whatever the angle between the coil axis and the field.

If the coil is small enough for the field to be considered uniform, then from Eqn(7.4), the flux through it:

$$\delta\Phi = \boldsymbol{B}.\delta\boldsymbol{A} = B\delta A\cos\theta$$

the coil response (e.m.f.) will be proportional to its rate of change.

Again because the field is considered uniform, the m.s.p.d. δU between the ends of the coil is given by $\boldsymbol{H}.\delta\boldsymbol{l}$, from Eqn(7.9), which is equal to $H\delta l\cos\theta$. In summary:

$$\delta\Phi = B\delta A\cos\theta = \mu_0 H\delta A\cos\theta$$
$$\delta U = H\delta l\cos\theta$$

From these:

$$\delta\Phi = \delta U\mu_0\delta A/\delta l$$

so for a particular coil, of fixed area and length, $\delta\Phi \propto \delta U$.

This probably seems of academic interest at present, but if many such coils are connected in series as a Rogowski spiral, the net response of the whole system is proportional to the m.s.p.d. between the ends of the spiral. Thus it can be used to investigate m.s.p.d.s in a magnetic field.

If a magnetic field is set up and the ends of the spiral are fixed somewhere within it, it is found that the shape of the rest of the spiral makes no difference at all to the response, justifying our use of magnetic scalar equipotential surfaces.

If the ends of the spiral are joined, the spiral measures not simply the m.s.p.d. between two points, but instead the m.m.f. around a particular path. Experiments carried out with such a spiral and a single-turn coil carrying current as in Fig. 7.9 show the following results:

(a) If the spiral does not link with the coil, there is no response, whatever the shape and position of the spiral;

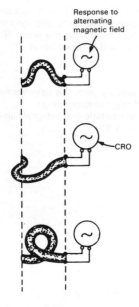

Response to alternating magnetic field

CRO

The ends must remain genuinely fixed. If we remove an end, wrap the spiral round a current and then replace the end we get a different answer. Magnetic scalar equipotential surfaces only apply for paths whose ends remain fixed, therefore.

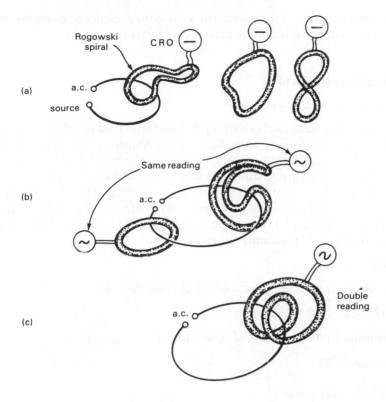

Fig. 7.9 Experiments with a Rogowski spiral.

(b) if the spiral links once with the coil, the same response is produced however the spiral and coil are positioned;

(c) if the spiral links several times with the coil, and/or if the coil has several turns, the response is proportional only to the total number of linkings. It is again unaffected by the topology, that is the shapes and positions of the coil and spiral;

(d) in cases (b) and (c), the response is also proportional to the current in the coil.

We can summarize these results by writing the m.m.f. as a loop integral, from Eqn(7.9), and showing that its value depends on the total current through the loop:

$$\oint H.dl = \Sigma NI \qquad (7.10)$$

where NI represents a current I passing through N turns, and the Σ shows that several current-carrying coils could be involved. To make the equation more general, Eqn(2.17) can be used to represent all the current passing through the loop, and Eqn(7.10) becomes:

$$\oint H.dl = \iint J.dA \qquad (7.11)$$

This is one way of writing **Ampere's law**.

Finally, we note that although a magnetic scalar potential difference between two points can be quoted, a unique 'magnetic scalar potential' cannot, because the

In a sense this has been done already, when m.m.f. was defined as number of turns × current in Chapter 6, but at that point we were concerned with the total flux produced not, as here, small parts of it.

Note that this equation is as yet incomplete and will be finished in Chapter 11. As before, in advanced work a differentiated form is used: curl $H = J$.

loop integral is not zero. Like the electric field in the presence of changing flux, the H field is non-conservative in the presence of currents.

Predicting Magnetic Fields

The field near a straight wire

We shall look at general methods of solving magnetic field problems in Chapter 8, but one useful result follows immediately from Ampere's law. This is the B field value at a perpendicular distance r from a straight wire which is so long that the rest of the circuit driving current down the wire is too far away to matter.

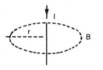

The wire carries a current I. We can find the loop integral for H simply by taking a circular path round the wire at a distance r. By symmetry, H must be independent of direction, so in Eqn (7.11) it can be brought outside the integral sign. The right hand side of Eqn(7.11) is simply the current I, so:

$$H \oint dl = I$$

$\oint dl$ is simply the circumference of the circular path, so

Note the direction of B fits the right-hand rule:

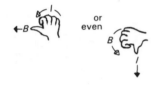

$$2\pi r H = I$$

Substituting from Eqn(7.8) and re-arranging:

$$B = \mu_0 \mu_r I / 2\pi r \tag{7.12}$$

The field of a long solenoid

n turns/*m* is equivalent to

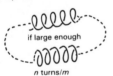

if large enough

n turns/*m*

The surroundings of a point well within a very long solenoid are indistinguishable from those within a toroid sufficiently large for its curvature not to be noticeable. If the current, I, and number of turns per metre, n, are the same for each, so also will be the separation of magnetic scalar equipotential surfaces, and so will be H, therefore.

For a toroid:

$$\begin{aligned} H = \text{m.m.f/length} &= \text{Total turns} \times \text{current/length} \\ &= \text{turns/metre} \times \text{current} \\ &= nI \end{aligned}$$

Thus, for a long solenoid also $H = nI$, so from Eqn(7.8):

$$B = \mu_0 \mu_r nI \tag{7.13}$$

Exercise 7.3

Prove that the B field at one end of a very long solenoid is just half the value in the middle. Hint: consider two very long solenoids placed end to end: it's another very long solenoid!

The field of a current element

Many field problems can be solved approximately by the magnetic circuit and scalar potential techniques discussed above, and often the intuitive understanding this gives may offset any imprecision in the detailed results.

Occasions do arise, however, where an accurate knowledge of a field is required, though this is more common in such areas as electron dynamics and aerial theory than in electronic circuit elements. For this, we must use a process similar to calculating electric fields from the inverse square law applied to all the charges present. In a few cases it can be done analytically, though more usually computing must be employed.

The smallest entity that could produce a magnetic field is called a current element, and is represented by an isolated wire of length δl along which a current I is flowing. This is clearly impossible in practice, as current has to be fed into and out of it.

The equation representing the field of a current element is called the Biot – Savart equation:

$$\delta B = \frac{\mu_0 \mu_r I(\delta l \times \hat{r})}{4\pi R^2} \qquad (7.14)$$

For the reasons just given, this is difficult to justify experimentally in isolation. However, if it is integrated to represent the field of a real circuit, it always predicts correctly.

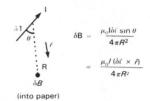

(into paper)

See Eqn(5.2) for an explanation of $\hat{r}$.

The oscillating current in a dipole aerial resembles a current element for distant observers, as long as the oscillation frequency is much lower than that for which the aerial is designed. Otherwise it sends out electromagnetic waves (see Chapter 11).

Worked Example 7.2

Show that the Biot – Savart equation correctly predicts the magnetic field due to a very long wire [Eqn(7.12)].

Solution: In Fig. 7.10, the contribution of length δl must be calculated, then integrated over the whole length. This is not defined, but the angle θ will change from 0 to 180°, so the integrating variable must be changed to θ:

$$\delta\theta = \delta l \sin\theta / R \qquad (7.15)$$

and $\quad r = R \sin\theta \qquad (7.16)$

δB produced by the current element δl is, from Eqn (7.14):

$$\delta B = \frac{\mu_0 \mu_r I \delta l \sin\theta}{4\pi R^2}$$

substituting from Eqns (7.15) and (7.16):

$$\delta B = \frac{\mu_0 \mu_r I \delta\theta \sin\theta}{4\pi r}$$

so $\quad B = \frac{\mu_0 \mu_r I}{4\pi r} \int_0^{180°} \sin\theta \, d\theta$

$$= \frac{\mu_0 \mu_r I}{2\pi r} \text{ as before}$$

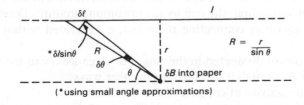

$$R = \frac{r}{\sin\theta}$$

(*using small angle approximations)

Fig. 7.10 Field near a long straight wire.

The Biot – Savart law can be applied to any realistic geometry of wires and its predictions checked by experiment. This is its justification.

Summary

The magnetic vector B is defined from $F = I(l \times B)$ and has units of tesla. It is also equal to the density of magnetic flux and can therefore be given units of Wb m^{-2}.

Mathematically the connection is $\Phi = \iint B.dA$.

Conservation of magnetic flux is represented by $\oiint B.dA = 0$.

The force F on a moving charged particle is given by $F = q(v \times B)$.

Lenz' law states that induced currents flow such as to generate fields opposing their cause.

Induced e.m.f. and changing field strength are connected by

$$\oint E.dl = - \frac{d}{dt} \left(\iint B.dA \right) \qquad \text{(Faraday's law)}$$

The motor and dynamo effects can be shown to depend on the same motion of electrons in a magnetic field.

At a point in a magnetic circuit, $B = \mu_0\mu_r dU/dl$, where U is the magnetic scalar potential. dU/dl is called H, the m.s.p. gradient. The H field is non-conservative in the present of currents.

Ampere's law for the field around a current can be stated as

$$\oint H.dl = \Sigma NI = \iint J.dA$$

The field near a straight wire is given by $B = \mu_0\mu_r I/2\pi r$, and of a toroid or very long solenoid $B = \mu_0\mu_r nI$ where n is turns/metre.

The Biot – Savart law for the field of a current element is

$$\delta B = \frac{\mu_0\mu_r I(\delta l \times r)}{4\pi R^2}$$

Problems

*Indicates more challenging problems or parts of problems.

7.1 Because of flux leakage, a B field of 0.01 T exists near a large d.c. motor. Calculate the force on a 2 m length of power supply cable carrying 10 A at right angles to this field.

7.2 A copper ring of mean diameter 40 mm is made from rod 8 mm diameter and rotates at 20 revolutions per second in a magnetic field of 0.2 T, such that the flux changes through the coil by the maximum amount. Determine:
  (a) the equation connecting the e.m.f. $\mathscr{E}$ generated within the ring with time t;
  *(b) the power dissipated in the ring. For elegance try to use power density $= J.E$, though it can be done in other ways.
    (Conductivity of copper is 6.3×10^7 S m^-)

7.3 Using a similar argument to that in Exercise 7.3, show that the H field at a perpendicular distance r from the end of a long wire is $I/4\pi r$.

*7.4 Integrate the Biot – Savart equation to find the H fields in the following cases:

(a) At a distance r from a conducting rod of length L, perpendicular to a point l from one end. Hint: convert the problem into an angle one, as in Worked Example 7.2 and note that the formula will apply when l is negative or $> L$ also. Hence find also the field at any point inside or outside a rectangular coil, in its plane.

(b) At the centre of a flat circular coil of radius a, N turns and carrying a current I.

(c) On the axis of the coil in (b), where the wire subtends an angle α to the axis. Note that each element will produce a field component perpendicular to the axis also but they will cancel when the whole coil is considered.

(d) At a point on the axis of a short solenoid, by integrating your answer to (c). Again use an angle as your variable. Extend your answer to fit a very long solenoid and compare with $H = nI$.

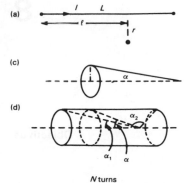

N turns

91

8 Inductance and Magnetic Materials

Objectives

☐ To introduce the circuit behaviour of magnetic components and relate this to their internal structure.

☐ To give a general method of approach to magnetic calculations.

☐ To estimate inductances of transformers, inductors and other simple circuit elements, also stray inductances.

☐ To describe the magnetization of strongly magnetic materials and suggest a domain model for understanding it.

☐ To discuss losses of both energy and flux in magnetic systems and look at ways of describing and reducing them.

☐ To show that large size is desirable in magnetic systems.

☐ To introduce magnetic bubbles.

Self and Mutual Inductance

Up to this point, we have regarded the source of magnetic flux and its detection as events taking place in two different pieces of equipment. At the start of Chapter 6, coil P generated flux and coil Q detected it and from that point on we have discussed the two operations separately.

Moreover, we have been concerned with the intimate details of field strengths and flux patterns, whereas for many applications of magnetic devices all we need to know are simply currents and induced p.d.s. If a device is being used as a circuit element an external description is more important than a knowledge of internal fields.

It is like the difference between needing to know the internal workings of an electrostatic device or merely its capacitance.

The external view

If a single coil is conducting d.c., the current sets up a magnetic field according to Eqn(6.3). Any p.d. across the coil is required only to drive the current against the coil resistance. If, however, the current is required to change, magnetic flux will also change in the coil, and by Eqn(7.7) an e.m.f. will be set up, which the energy source will need to supply in addition to the p.d. simply to overcome the coil resistance. This effect, of a circuit requiring extra p.d. in order to cause a rate of change of current through itself, is called **self-induction**, and is described by:

Although the term 'coil' is used here, any conductor that generates a magnetic field will have associated self and mutual inductances. This also applies to real resistors and capacitors. Wirewound resistors, unless wound with half the turns in reversed sense, and electrolytic capacitors should not be used at high frequencies.

$$\mathcal{E} = -L\,dI/dt \qquad (8.1)$$

where L is called the **coefficient of self-inductance** or, often, simply 'inductance'. The minus sign represents Lenz' law, as the induced e.m.f. will act against any applied p.d. which is attempting to increase the current I.

Signs can be easily confused in this situation. Keep Lenz' law and a physical picture in your mind always!

J. Henry discovered self-induction in 1830. The henry is also equivalent to the Wb A^{-1}.

By re-arranging Eqn(8.1), the unit of self-inductance can be seen to be the V s A^{-1}, which usually termed the **henry** (H).

A similar equation can be produced for the case first studied in Chapter 6, where the changing flux from one coil generates an e.m.f. in another. In this case suffixes are required to distinguish the coils. If coil 2 generates flux and coil 1 detects it:

$$\mathcal{E}_1 = L_{12} dI_2/dt \tag{8.2a}$$

where L_{12} is called the **coefficient of mutual inductance** for coil 2 affecting coil 1. L_{12} may have a negative sign if an increasing current in coil 2 causes a negative induced e.m.f. in coil 1, but a sign convention is required on diagrams to make this clear.

Clearly, these arguments are reversible, so L_{21} can be defined from the e.m.f. in coil 2 generated by a changing current in coil 1:

$$\mathcal{E}_2 = L_{21} dI_1/dt \tag{8.2b}$$

If currents are allowed to flow in both coils, each will experience a mutual e.m.f., in addition to the one produced by its own changing current.

Apparently, both coefficients of mutual inductance L_{12} and L_{21} are needed in calculations, but it is possible to show that they are always equal, so they are replaced by the single coefficient M.

This equivalence of L_{12} and L_{21} is not intuitively obvious, but can be justified from linearity considerations (see Carter, chapter 6).

Conventionally, the equations are written not in terms of the induced e.m.f.s but of the p.d.s required across the coils to allow the current changes to occur. This has the advantage that the effect of circuit resistance can be added in more easily if required:

$$\text{applied p.d.} \quad \begin{aligned} V_1 &= L_1 dI_1/dt + M dI_2/dt \ (+ R_1 I_1) \\ V_2 &= M dI_1/dt + L_2 dI_2/dt \ (+ R_2 I_2) \end{aligned} \Bigg\} \tag{8.3}$$

The internal view

From our earlier work on magnetic circuits, we can obtain a relationship between the self- and mutual-inductances and the magnetic properties of the coil(s) involved. This will clearly allow the design of coils of specified circuit properties, and also the calculation of stray inductances due to wires and printed circuit board tracks, which can cause problems in pulse and high-frequency circuits.

Inductance between printed circuit tracks are discussed later in this chapter and, along with earth loops, in Carter, chapter 6. For an account of the problems such inductances cause see Horowitz and Hill, chapters 9 and 13.

Consider the self-inductance case first. Combining Eqn(8.1) and Eqn(6.1):

$$L dI/dt = N d\Phi/dt$$

So for a small change in current δI causing a change in flux $\delta\Phi$:

$$L = N\delta\Phi/\delta I$$

From Eqn(6.3):

$$M = NI = S\Phi$$

If S is constant:

$$N\delta I = S\delta\Phi \qquad \text{so } \delta\Phi/\delta I = N/S \qquad \text{and so:}$$

$$L = N^2/S \tag{8.4}$$

Thus the self-inductance of an electric circuit that generates flux can be obtained from the number of turns within the circuit and the reluctance of the magnetic path followed by the flux generated.

Units of S and μ_0 follow from this also. N has no units, so the unit of reluctance is

H^{-1}. As for a simple magnetic circuit $S = l/\mu_0 A$, the unit of μ_0 is clearly that of l/SA, which is $H\ m^{-1}$.

Exercise 8.1 Calculate the self-inductance of the magnetizing coil in Worked Example 7.1. Take the cross-sectional diameter as 0.15 m.
(Answer: $L = 0.386\ H$)

For the case of two coils, a similar derivation to that giving Eqn(8.4) produces an equation:

$$M = N_1 N_2 / S_m \tag{8.5}$$

It is perhaps surprising that the reluctance of a magnetic path between two coils is always the same for each, but remember that the flux involved is the mutual flux from one to the other, which may be only a small fraction of the total flux made:

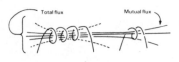

Note the terms primary and secondary are reversible and apply to a transformer only when used in a circuit. A transformer made to step down from mains 240 V to 12 V can be used in reverse, with a car-battery powered oscillator, to generate 'mains' for fluorescent lights in a caravan, for instance.

Surprisingly, the flux in a transformer core does not depend on the current taken as Lenz' law ensures it is kept within limits. It only represents leakage flux in fact, and an ideal transformer would have no core flux whatever!

Inductors, with or without a material core, are used mainly in switched-mode power supplies (see Horowitz and Hill, chapter 5) and in high frequency circuits.

where S_m is the mutual reluctance of the path between coil 2 and coil 1. An equation with 1 and 2 reversed can be generated also, of course, with the same value of S_m.

A component made up of two or more coils magnetically coupled together is called a **transformer**. It usual function is to couple a changing current in one circuit into another circuit, using flux as an intermediary.

The perfect transformer as a circuit component

If the whole of the flux change generated by one coil, called the **primary winding**, passes through the other, **secondary winding**, the e.m.f. across each winding will be proportional to the number of turns N_p and N_s, respectively. In the primary this represents an e.m.f. $\mathscr{E}_p$ to be overcome by the driving circuit in order to maintain the flux change, while in the secondary it is the e.m.f. $\mathscr{E}_s$ actually driving current:

$$\mathscr{E}_s / \mathscr{E}_p = N_s / N_p \tag{8.6}$$

If current I_s flows from the secondary into a load, then by Lenz' law it will generate flux that reduces the flux change causing it. $\mathscr{E}_p$ will be reduced, allowing the source to drive a current I_p to build up the flux to its former value. By considering the conservation of power in primary and secondary circuits, it should be clear that ignoring losses:

$$\mathscr{E}_p I_p = \mathscr{E}_s I_s \tag{8.7}$$

Thus a transformer which steps voltage up by the ratio N_s / N_p steps current down by the same ratio. In practice, losses make the secondary e.m.f. less and the primary current more than calculated.

Air-cored Inductors

Inductors are components whose main contribution to an electric circuit is to generate an e.m.f. proportional to the rate of change of current through them. Real components will have in addition d.c. resistance and also capacitance, both between the turns and to other nearby conductors, which complicates their behaviour at high frequencies.

Small-value inductors are usually made from up to several tens of turns of wire on a plastic former, though those of very low value may be self-supporting coils of a few turns of relatively thick wire.

Because they are air-cored, with no strongly magnetic material to act as 'conductors' of flux, and because often the turns are well separated, the inductance of such coils is not easy to predict accurately, as flux will escape from the sides. More-over, if the turns are wound in several layers, the reluctance of the inner layers will be different from those further out, again making calculation awkward.

However, a rough guide can be obtained by considering the way the magnetic scalar potential will vary around the magnetic circuit. Within the coil, the flux lines will be close, showing that B is relatively large and so will H be also. Outside, however, the flux has effectively the whole of space to occupy, and diverges rapidly from the ends. B and H will be small, therefore. Thus the magnetic scalar potential will fall rapidly through the coil, but only very slowly outside. Most of the magnetic potential drop will be inside the coil, so most of the reluctance of the magnetic circuit must also be inside the coil.

So to a first approximation, the reluctance of an air-cored solenoid is equal to the reluctance of the path through its middle, and the effect of the surrounding region can be ignored. The longer the coil relative to its diameter, the better is this approximation.

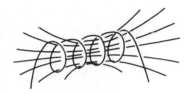

For a ferrite cored inductor this simple approach does not work, because the reluctance of the core is itself quite low, comparable with or even less than the reluctance of the path outside the coil.

Estimate the number of turns required on a former 20 mm long and of diameter 5 mm to make a coil of self-inductance 4μH.
(Answer: 57 turns using approximation; accurate calculations give an answer of 60 turns, assuming a single layer is used.)

Exercise 8.2

Calculations in Magnetism

The strategy for carrying out calculations in this area is similar to that discussed in Chapter 4 for electrostatics. A similar diagram can be drawn, in fact, such as Fig. 8.1. The diagram is more complex than Fig. 4.9 because more concepts are used in magnetism. In particular, L can be found from S directly, using Eqn(8.4), whereas there is no commonly used equivalent of S in electrostatics.

Note that Eqn(8.1) would need integrating to give the relationship for L shown here.

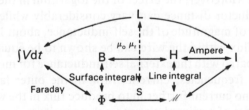

Fig. 8.1 Magnetism calculations diagram.

Find the inductance per unit length of coaxial cable, whose inner conductor is of radius a and outer of radius A. Ignore flux generated within the inner conductor and assume the insulation has no magnetic effect.

Solution: The current in the outer conductor exactly neutralizes the effect of the inner current as far as the region outside is concerned, so only the circular flux between the conductors contributes to the self-inductance.

The inner and outer conductors and whatever connects them electrically at the ends of the cable form a single-turn coil in effect, so from Eqn(8.4) the inductance

Worked Example 8.1

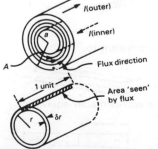

per unit length will be the reciprocal of the reluctance per unit length of the path to the circular flux.

Reluctance of thin cylindrical path of radius r and thickness δr:

$$= 2\pi r / (\mu_0 \times l \times \delta r)$$

So inductance of a cable whose conductors define this path:

$$= \mu_0 \delta r / 2\pi r$$

Inductance per unit length of actual cable:

$$= \int_a^A \mu_0 \, dr / 2\pi r$$

Note the logarithm factor, as in the capacitance of a coaxial cable found in Worked Example 4.3.

$$= \frac{\mu_0 \ln(A/a)}{2\pi} \qquad (8.8)$$

'Stray' inductance

The inductance of wires and printed circuit tracks can cause problems at high frequencies and in digital circuits, particularly when circuit or stray capacitances combine with stray inductance to produce resonance at frequencies of interest.

Resonance: see Yorke, chapter 3. In general, resonance occurs at a frequency f_r given by $f_r = 1/2\pi \sqrt{(LC)}$, so for example a stray capacitance of 2 pF combined with a stray inductance of 0.1 μH can give problems around 350 MHz.

Most situations involving strays are of complex geometry, but the actual inductance value is unlikely to be required to any great accuracy. Rough, semi-intuitive methods are often adequate and, moreover, can lead to a better understanding than solving equations or running computer programmes.

The **external self-inductance of a single wire** is apparently infinite! This can be seen by considering the wire as the inner conductor of a coaxial cable whose outer conductor goes to infinity, and using the answer to Worked Example 8.1. The reason for the paradox is that a single wire carrying without a return path is not possible, of course. Moreover, the effect of the logarithm in the expression means that the outer conductor distance can vary considerably while making little difference to the order of magnitude of the self-inductance, about 1 μH m^{-1}. The self-inductance due to flux within the wire can be shown to be equal to $\mu_0/8\pi$ H m^{-1}, which is small compared with the external self-inductance for most 'isolated' wires. Moreover, at high frequencies, currents flow in the outer layers only of conductors, so there is no current further in to produce flux in the wire material itself.

For an inner conductor diameter d, and ignoring the flux inside the wire, Eqn(8.5) gives answers as follows for different outer diameters:

10 d: 0.46 μH m^{-1}
1000 d: 1.38 μH m^{-1}
1 000 000 d: 2.76 μH m^{-1}

so to state that the external self-inductance of an isolated wire is about 1 μH m^{-1} is not unreasonable in practice!

See Worked Example 8.5 and Duffin, chapter 9. The answer assumes uniform current flux.

This is the 'skin effect', which causes resistance problems at high frequencies, as only the outer layer of a conductor is used. See Duffin, chapter 9.

The self-inductance of a printed-circuit track opposite an earth or ground plane can be estimated by considering it as a one-turn solenoid. If the track width is w and the insulation depth d, the reluctance per unit track length of the flux path between track and ground plane is given approximately by:

$$S = w / (\mu_0 \times d \times l)$$

As there is effectively only one turn, the inductance per unit length L_m is given by:

$$L_m = \mu_0 d / w$$

For example, a 0.6 mm width track on 1.6 mm board thickness has from this a predicted self-inductance of approximately $4\pi \times 10^{-7} \times 1.6/0.6 = 3.4$ μH m^{-1}.

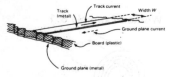

is equivalent to:

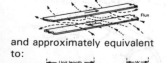

and approximately equivalent to:

Estimate the resonant frequency due to self-inductance and capacitance of 100 mm of 0.6 mm width track separated from a ground plance by 1.6 mm of epoxy board, of relative permittivity 3. The resonant frequency f_r is given by

Exercise 8.3

$$f_r = \frac{1}{2\pi\sqrt{(LC)}}$$

(Answer: f_r = 275 MHz)

The most straightforward situations have been chosen for calculation in this introductory book. The more subtle problems of calculating capacitances and mutual inductance between adjacent tracks on a board are dealt with in more advanced texts, but the order of magnitude of the numbers is usually of the order of picofarads and microhenries per metre for stray capacitances and inductances, respectively.

Carter, chapter 6, deals with this in more depth.

Magnetization

At the beginning of Chapter 6, a magnetic material was defined as one that can influence the quantity of magnetic flux produced by a current. As in the electrostatic case, the effect can be described either in terms of a multiplier, μ_r in this case, or by considering an additional field set up by the material, similar to the polarization field in electrostatics.

In Eqn(7.8), $B = \mu_0 \mu_r H$, the additional field produced by the material can be separated from the field that would exist anyway by writing it as:

$$B = \mu_0 H + M \qquad (8.9)$$

where M is called the **magnetic polarization** of the material, and will clearly have the tesla as its unit. It represents additional flux density manufactured by the material. M can either be temporary, existing only in the presence of H, or can have some permanence, retaining at least part of its value when H is removed, as will be discussed later in this chapter.

Several types of magnetic material exist, but for engineering applications ferromagnetics and ferrimagnetics are the most important at present. Lack of space forbids the discussion of the other types in this book.

M is analogous to P in electrostatics. It is sometimes called 'magnetization', also 'intensity of magnetization', also 'magnetic moment per unit volume'! If M depends only on H it can be written as $M = \mu_0 \chi H$, where χ (chi) is called magnetic susceptibility. χ is only of use with weak, non-remanent materials and rarely applied to ferromagnetics.

See, e.g., Solymar and Walsh, chapter 11, for other kinds of magnetism.

Strongly magnetic materials

Materials that retain some magnetization when an applied H has been removed are called either ferromagnetics or ferrimagnetics. The differences between these at the atomic level are fairly subtle, but an understanding in depth is not necessary at this stage. A simple model will be described after we have looked at the results of experimental work on these materials.

Experiments can be set up, perhaps using a ring of material, in which an H field can be applied whose size is known from current and geometry measurements, and the resulting B field in the material measured, from e.m.f.s induced when it changes. If the material starts from a completely demagnetized state, in other words no M is detectable, a plot of B against H can be obtained that, if H can be made large enough, looks like Fig. 8.2(a). This shows the '$B - H$ curve' for a representative sample of iron and also for air, though not to the same scale.

Four points are worth noting about this **initial magnetization curve**:

Ferromagnetics are simply 'like iron' and include cobalt, nickel and some garnets. Ferrimagnetics are 'like ferrites' and include other mixed oxides containing iron. Solymar and Walsh, chapter 11, gives a more complete description.

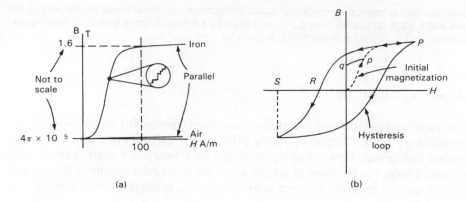

Fig. 8.2   Examples of $B - H$ curves.

This would be a 'chord' value of μ_r. The 'slope' value, useful for small changes, would be much less.

(a) The value of B achieved is about 5000 times greater than for air at the same H field. μ_r is thus 5000 at that field.

(b) The gradient near the orgin is relatively gentle, getting gradually steeper until the behaviour discussed as point (c).

(c) Eventually a limiting value of B is reached, called the **saturation B field**.

(d) If the graph is examined very closely, it is found to increase in steps.

On reducing H to zero, the graph in Fig. 8.2(a) is found to be non-reversible. Instead, part PQ of the graph Fig. 8.2(b) is followed, showing that the iron remains magnetized after H has been removed. The B field at Q is called the **retentivity** of the material if it was magnetized to saturation initially. If a lower point, such as p, were chosen when H was removed, q would be reached instead; some B field remains but not the maximum possible.

Also called remanent B field or remanence.

If H is switched off at R, some B remains, depending on the geometry of the specimen, so the magnetization is not removed completely by this process. Carter explains this more fully in chapter 5.

'Hysteresis' comes from a Greek word meaning delay and represents the way changes in B lag behind those in H.

If the H field is now reversed, the graph continues down to R in the saturated case. This represents the H field required to make the magnetization zero within a saturation loop and is termed the **coercivity** of the material.

If the H field is increased negatively to S, decreased to zero, then increased once again to a large positive value, a complete, symmetrical loop called a **hysteresis loop** is generated as shown by the whole of Fig. 8.2(b). The loop drawn represents only one possible magnetization path for the material, the saturation loop. An infinite variety of loop shapes is possible, depending on the way H changes. In particular, to demagnetize a specimen reliably, it needs to be exposed to an a.c. H field of gradually decreasing amplitude, generating loops that become gradually smaller until they disappear.

In Chapter 9 we shall discuss in detail the energy changes when a material is cycled through a hysteresis loop. The larger the loop area, the greater the energy lost per cycle.

Hard and soft materials

The saturation hysteresis loops of strong magnetic materials show a wide variation. For engineering purposes two particular classes of loop are employed. These are:

(a) Tall narrow loops. These 'soft' materials are readily magnetized, with a large μ_r value, and equally readily lose their magnetization when the H field is removed, as they have a small coercivity. They include pure iron, if of large grain size, and specially made alloys of iron, silicon and nickel, as well as certain ferrites. Trade names include Supermalloy, Permalloy and Mumetal. As the loop areas are small, so also will be the energy lost per cycle, so these materials are used where changing fields are involved, such as in transformer cores and some parts of electromagnetic machinery.

(b) Loops of large area. Such 'hard' materials retain their magnetization even in the presence of moderate fields and are thus used to make permanent magnets. High-carbon fine grained steel works moderately well, but alloys of aluminium, nickel and cobalt are much better, as are some ferrites. Alnico and Ferroxdur are among the commercial names used.

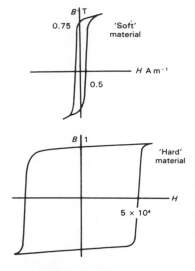

The properties of materials making them 'soft' and 'hard' magnetically tend to make them soft or hard mechanically also; large grain size makes for 'softness' in both senses, for example.

Simple domain theory of magnetization

In depth, magnetization is still not properly understood, and for even a little detailed knowledge some quantum theory and statistical mechanics are required. In this book, a simple intuitive model will be introduced, which is essentially correct but not rigorous.

The atoms of a strongly magnetic material act as permanent magnets, which line up pointing the same way over a substantial region, called a domain. If the material is found to be demagnetized, with no externally measurable M, this is because the domains arrange themselves in tiny magnetic circuits, holding all their magnetic flux in a continuous loop and allowing none to escape, as in Fig. 8.3(a).

If an H field is applied, the energy of domains with a component of M opposite to H is increased whereas that of domains magnetized in the same direction as H is reduced. This causes the latter to increase in area at the expense of the former, as shown in Fig. 8.3(b). The change is produced by a reversal in M direction by atoms at the domain boundary. Eventually the whole region, which started as a circuit of domains, ends up as one domain as in Fig. 8.3(c). If H continues to increase, the M direction within each domain itself changes to be parallel to H, as Fig. 8.3(d) shows.

The theory explains the general shape of the $B – H$ curve in Fig. 8.2 as follows.

The first movements of the domain boundaries have only a small effect on B, as the reluctance of the tiny circuits remains low, allowing little flux to escape. Later, as the diminishing domains are 'squeezed' by the growing ones, the asymmetry releases more leakage flux, steepening the curve. Eventually, more and more domains point fully in the direction of H until no further increase in B is possible and the material saturates. The process is not continuous as the wall movements

See, e.g., Solymar and Walsh, chapter 11, and Duffin, chapter 12, for more detail. All the statements here can be justified experimentally: domain walls have been observed moving under the influence of an H field and the discontinuous changes mentioned can be connected with known irregularities in specimens. Large-grained materials tend to be 'soft' whereas very fine-grained materials are used for permanent magnets.

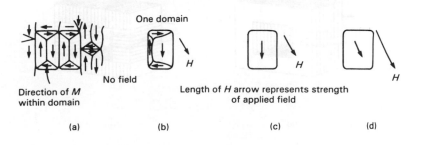

Fig. 8.3 Simple magnetic domain theory.

have to cross impurities, alloy precipitates and strained areas in the material crystal, all of which requires energy and makes the movements non-reversible. Thus the magnetization is in steps and demagnetization requires H to be reversed, not merely removed. This leads to the hysteresis effect.

Electromagnetic Machinery

As this book is directed mainly at students involved in the 'light current' end of electrical engineering, few structural details of electromagnetic machinery will be given. However, some general principles can be stated, following from the work done so far, which apply to all kinds of magnetic systems and should aid understanding of transformers and of both large and small machines.

In general, the primary design aim for electromagnetic machinery is to keep the efficiency high and the size small. This section will therefore concentrate on reducing losses both of energy and of flux, the former affecting running costs the latter the size and, therefore, the initial cost of a unit.

Energy losses

There are three main causes of energy loss in an electromagnetic machine:

> The losses are sometimes divided into copper losses (resistive and eddy current) and iron losses (eddy current and hysteresis).

(a) Resistive loss, due to heat in the ohmic resistance of windings from intentional currents flowing. These can be reduced by using wires as thick as possible, though this must be balanced against the high cost of copper.

> Carter, chapter 6, shows how the magnitude of eddy current losses can be estimated.

(b) Eddy current loss in the presence of changing fields, due to induced currents in all metals present, but particularly the components of the magnetic circuit. To reduce this, transformer cores are made in the form of flat plates, called laminations, separated from each other by non-conducting varnish to increase the core resistance to these currents.

Exercise 8.4   Show why Fig. 8.4(a) is a more satisfactory design for a laminated-core transformer than is Fig. 8.4(b). Give two reasons, one involving reluctance, the other eddy currents.

In transformer cores for use at high frequencies, ferrites are used, which are electrically insulating and thus avoid the eddy current problem completely. There is a price to be paid in the rather lower values of μ_r and of saturation B field for these materials.

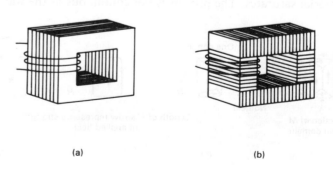

(a)   (b)

Fig. 8.4   Alternative arrangements of core laminations for Exercise 8.4.

(c) Hysteresis loss, again in the presence of changing fields. As explained above, the magnetization of a material uses up some energy, as the domain wall movement is not reversible. It will be shown in Chapter 9 that the energy loss is directly proportional to the hysteresis loop area, so a magnetically 'soft' material should be used.

Flux problems

Two problems will be discussed, saturation and flux leakage.

All materials have a limit to the B field they can produce, as has been described already. In any design of a magnetic circuit, H fields must be kept below the value which would cause saturation. As soon as saturation occurs, the change in B for a given change in $\mu_0 H$, the slope, dynamic or differential permeability, will reduce to 1 and for changes in H above this value the material is no better than air. For very large magnetic fields, above a few teslas, ferromagnetics are useless, in fact, and other techniques must be used.

In most machines, and in transformers by definition, flux is required to be coupled from one coil to another. The proportion of flux that links both coils, as compared with the total amount generated, can be described by a **coupling coefficient**, k. It is more convenient to define k in terms of inductance and reluctance rather than flux, as it depends on materials and geometries rather than actual current values.

If the coupling between two coils is perfect, the magnetic circuit must be exactly common to both, so a single value of reluctance S applies to flux generated by either and detected by either. The self-inductances L_1 and L_2 and the mutual inductance M can be related, using the number of turns N_1 and N_2 in each coil, by:

$$M = N_1 N_2 / S$$
$$L_1 = N_1{}^2 / S$$
$$L_2 = N_2{}^2 / S$$

Thus for perfect coupling:

$$M = \sqrt{(L_1 L_2)}$$

If the coupling is less than perfect, M will be smaller than this and k can be shown to fit the equation:

$$M = k\sqrt{(L_1 L_2)} \tag{8.10}$$

For most power transformers and electrical machinery, k is close to 1, often above 0.99.

If a certain flux is required in a secondary coil, extra flux has to be made in the primary to correct for any flux lost. More turns are required than would otherwise be the case, adding to the cost and size. Leakage flux does not by itself involve a loss in energy, but the requirement to make extra flux will cause additional energy losses by the paths already described.

Leakage flux is minimized by keeping the series reluctance as low as possible, thus ensuring the path for flux through magnetic material is easy relative to the path through air.

Worked Example 8.4 shows how a gap in a magnetic circuit can help prevent this.

See Duffin, chapter, 12 for the production of very large magnetic fields.

In induction motors the second 'coil' is a path within solid metal through which eddy currents flow, but the principle still applies. See Laithwaite.

There will be a second order dependence on currents, of course, as μ_r itself is a function of H for strongly magnetic materials.

This relationship is proved in Carter, chapter 6, which also shows how leakage flux can be estimated. For high-frequency transformers used for coupling wide bandwidth signals, there are advantages in using coils of low, though known, coupling, as Duffin, chapter 10, shows.

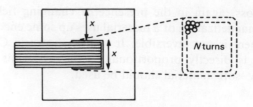

Depth (dimension into page) also x

Fig. 8.5 Inductor for scaling calculations.

Scaling effects — big is beautiful

In Chapter 5 we found that electrostatic machines are required to be small to be effective, as electrostatics is a surface phenomenon. Conversely, we shall see now that electromagnetic machines are better the larger they are, as magnetism is a volume effect.

Many machine properties can be reduced to the effective self-inductance of a winding on a core, so this will be taken as an example. A good inductor must have several properties:

(a) Its ratio of inductance to resistance should be high, to keep down resistive energy losses.
(b) Its core should not saturate at the maximum current desired.
(c) It should be as small as possible.

Figure 8.5 shows a simple inductor with N turns occupying the maximum space, to ensure wire as thick as possible can be used. For convenience the central hole is square, of the same side length as the width of the core. The core depth, into the page, is also x, so x defines the scale of the inductor.

We shall find its resistance, reluctance and self-inductance, and determine how these change if the scale factor x changes with N kept constant.

From Eqn(2.11):

An 'average' turn is a square of side $2x$, so average length of turns is $8x$.

$$\text{Resistance } R = \rho l/A = \rho 8Nx/(x^2/N)$$
$$= \rho 8N^2/x$$

So for a given N, R is inversely proportional to x.

From Eqn(6.4):

$$\text{Reluctance } S = 1/\mu_0\mu_r A = 8x/\mu_0\mu_r x^2$$
$$= 8/\mu_0\mu_r x$$

S is also inversely proportional to x thus L, which is equal to N^2/S, will be proportional to x.

Combining these:

The ratio $L/R = \mu_0\mu_r x^2/64\,\rho$

The ratio L/R is therefore very strongly dependent on the scaling factor x.

The quality factor, Q, used in a.c. theory, is equal to $\omega L/R$, so high-Q inductors for low frequencies are difficult to make of small size. See Yorke, chapter 3.

If the material has a saturation B value B_s, the current I required to saturate is given by:

$$I = SAB_s/N$$

$$= 8B_s x/\mu_0\mu_r N$$

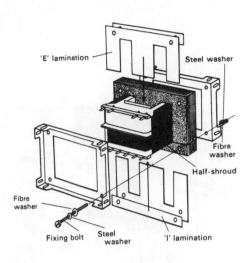

'E' lamination

Steel washer

Fibre
washer

Half-shroud

Fibre
washer

Fixing bolt

Steel
washer

'I' lamination

Fig. 8.6   Transformer system (courtesy RS Components Ltd).

So an inductor required to pass a given current before saturation will need to be of size proportional to the current.

In each case, therefore, the larger the inductor, the better its performance. However, remember that if the scaling factor is doubled, for instance, the volume and therefore material cost will increase eight times.

Some Applications

This brief section will concentrate on the kind of component commonly met by electronic engineers rather than those for power engineering.

See Grossner for further details of transformers used in electronics.

Low-frequency power transformers

These are usually wound on a double-O core, apart from some very high-quality expensive ones wound on a toroid. The core is made from laminations of iron containing a few percent silicon. Figure 8.6 shows the construction of a transformer in kit form.

High-frequency and pulse transformers

Figure 8.7 shows a high-frequency transformer in kit form, also based on a

properties of core assemblies at 25 °C

	symbol	RM6
Inductance Factor	AL	160
(nH/Turns²)		±2%
Turns Factor	α	79·06
(turns for 1mH)		±1%
Effective Permeability	μ_e	109·5
Temp. Coeff. of μ_e		51 min.
(+25 to 55 °C) ppm/°C		154 max.
Adjuster Range		+20%
Max. Residual plus Eddy Current Core Loss		
Tangent tan δ_{r+f} at 30 kHz		$0·34 \times 10^{-3}$
at 100 kHz		$0·58 \times 10^{-3}$
Recommended		
Frequency Range (kHz)		5·5 to 800
Energy Storage Capability (mJ)	LI²sat	0·383
B_{sat}	mT	250

magnetic properties of cores

	symbol	RM6
Effective Path Length	l_e	26·9 mm
Effective Path Area	A_e	31·3 mm²
Effective Volume	V_e	840 mm³

Fig. 8.7 Ferrite-cored transformer system (courtesy RS Components Ltd).

For a detailed account of bubble memories see Solymar and Walsh, chapter 11, and Bolton, chapter 22.

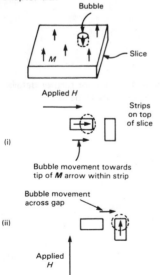

double-O core. Ferrite is used, for the reasons given earlier. It is a brittle material, and as an insulator does not need to be laminated, so it is supplied in two moulded halves. The values of μ_r and saturation B are smaller than the corresponding values for ferromagnetic materials.

Magnetic bubbles

Garnet is a family of minerals often used as semi-precious stones. Some members, such as yttrium iron garnet, are ferromagnetic, with a fairly wide hysteresis loop and μ_r large in one particular direction within the crystal. A thin slice is cut across this direction and magnetically saturated with its M vector normal to the plane of the slice. By applying a very localized field, a single domain a few micrometres wide can be produced with its magnetization in the opposite sense and which remains after the localized field is switched off; this is a magnetic bubble. Because the preferred direction of M is normal to the slice, a transverse field above it does not rotate the magnetization within the bubble, instead it moves the whole bubble sideways. Permalloy strips in a pattern on the slice concentrate the field locally and make the bubbles move along a defined path. By creating a bubble to represent a binary '1', and regarding its absence as binary '0', a chain of binary digits can be fed into the path, which can thus act as a memory. Although bubble memories have not so far produced quite the revolution in medium-speed computer storage that was expected, their time may yet come.

Summary

The coefficient of self-inductance L is defined from:

$\mathscr{E} = -L dI/dt$; its unit is the henry.

The coefficient of mutual inductance M between two coils is defined from $\mathscr{E}_1 = M dI_2/dt$ and applies equally if the suffixes are reversed.

The external and internal aspects of L and M are connected by:

$L = N^2/S$ and $M = N_1 N_2/S_m$

For a perfect transformer:

$N_s/N_p = \mathscr{E}_s/\mathscr{E}_p = I_p/I_s$

A long air-cored inductor has a reluctance approximately equal to the reluctance of the path down its own centre.

Stray inductances are of the order of microhenries metre^{-1} and stray capacitances of picofarads metre^{-1}.

For a magnetic material:

$\mathbf{B} = \mu_0 \mu_r \mathbf{H} = \mu_0 \mathbf{H} + \mathbf{M}$

Strongly magnetic materials can produce a B field up to a certain saturation value, and show hysteresis when the applied H is cycled.

'Soft' materials have a narrow hysteresis loop and are readily demagnetized; 'hard' materials, which retain their magnetization well, have a broad loop.

The behaviour of strongly magnetic materials can be modelled by the domain theory.

Magnetic systems can lose energy by resistance, eddy currents and hysteresis, and can leak flux also. Large systems work better than small for a given specification.

Coefficient of coupling k between two coils is obtained from:

$M = k \sqrt{(L_1 L_2)}$

Low-frequency transformers have silicon–iron laminated cores, high frequency use ferrite. Magnetic bubbles can store binary information in a memory device.

Problems

*Indicates more challenging problems.

8.1 A soft iron core of material of $\mu_r = 3000$ is to be used for inductors or transformers.
   (a) Explain why the design Fig. 8.8(a) is better than Fig. 8.8(b) for a given window size and core mass, for coils round the central bar. You can argue this intuitively, but check by estimating the reluctance in each case, noting that there are two magnetic circuits in parallel. Neglect flux curvature at the corners.
   (b) Making sensible estimates of the average flux path lengths, calculate the reluctance of the core in Fig. 8.8(a) to flux generated by a coil wrapped as in part (a).

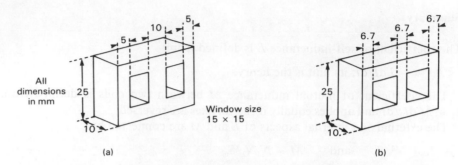

Fig. 8.8 Core design for Problem 8.1.

   (c) If the coil around the central bar has 1500 turns, estimate its self inductance and its mutual inductance to a coil of 100 turns round one of the outer bars. Assume no leakage.

8.2 Using the core design in Fig. 8.5, find the smallest value of x that will enable the production of a coil of self inductance 10 H and maximum d.c. current 1 A. If 60% of the area of the hole in the core can be filled with turns, calculate also the number of turns of wire, its thickness and the coil resistance. The relative permeability of the core material is 3000 and its saturation B 1.2 T. The resistivity of copper is 1.7×10^{-8} Ωm.

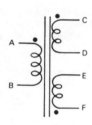

8.3 In the marginal figure, the dot convention is used to indicate which ends of transformer windings will be of the same polarity when a flux change occurs in the core. Determine the polarities CD and EF when positive current is flowing in at A and decreasing.

*8.4 Figure 8.9 shows two ferrite C-cores, each with a coil, and the B – H curve of the core material. Each coil has 100 turns, and the cores can be clamped either as shown, to make a complete ferrite magnetic circuit, or with spacers of thickness 0.1mm at x and y, keeping the two Cs apart.

   (a) What is μ_r and the self-inductance of one coil at an H field of 40 A m^{-1}, when no gap exists? Treat the hysteresis loop width as small.

   (b) With the cores clamped together, a d.c. current is passed through coil A, and the self-inductance B is measured using a small signal. Estimate this self-inductance at currents in A of 6.5 mA, 50 mA and 200 mA.

   (c) Repeat part (b) for the core with spacers.

*8.5 Show, by taking shells within a wire, that the self-inductance of a wire due to flux generated internally is equal to $\mu_0/8\pi$ H m^{-1}.

8.6 Show that the ferrite core data in Fig. 8.7 is self-consistent, perhaps by calculating L directly and then from the dimensions and μ_r value.

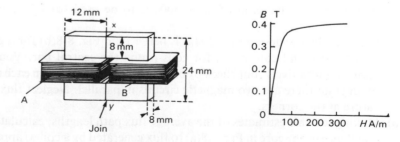

Fig. 8.9 *C*-core data for Problem 8.4.

Magnetic Energy and Force 9

Objectives

- [ ] To write a more complete expression for the e.m.f. of an inductive system, and from this find equations for magnetic energy transfers.
- [ ] To show how a force results from systems whose reluctance can change.
- [ ] To describe electromagnetic circuit breakers.
- [ ] To introduce reluctance minimization as a guide to understanding field shapes.
- [ ] To show how permanent magnet behaviour can be understood from magnetic circuit theory.
- [ ] To apply the motor effect to a coil expriencing torque and to a moving coil loudspeaker and to show how it leads to a definition of the ampere.

There are two approaches to magnetic force. One is the direct one, using $F = I(l \times B)$ or $F = q(v \times B)$. This can only be used when the resulting motion of wire or particle has little effect on the applied field. In any other case, the force must be calculated by differentiating an expression for potential energy.

This is similar to calculating electrostatic force in Chapter 5.

This could happen either because it generated noticeable flux or because an alteration in the reluctance of the magnetic circuit resulted in some way from the movement.

Magnetic Energy

As with electrostatics, we shall work our way to field energy starting from circuit ideas. However, we need first a more complete expression than Eqn(8.1) for the e.m.f. generated in self-induction. L was assumed constant at that stage, but this need not happen, of course. Experiment shows that if a core is drawn out of a coil carrying a current there is a force pulling it back in, so clearly an energy change is involved.

From Eqn(6.1):

$$\mathcal{E} = -N d\Phi/dt$$

Φ itself can be obtained in terms of L by using Eqns (6.3) and (8.4), giving:

$$\Phi = \frac{NI}{S} = \frac{LI}{N} \tag{9.1}$$

thus:

$$\epsilon = -N \frac{d\Phi}{dt} = -\frac{d(LI)}{dt} = -\frac{L dI}{dt} - \frac{I dL}{dt} \tag{9.2}$$

N could be changing also, if turns were being added to or removed from a coil, but this is not a common event! All the equations from now on assume N constant.

Now we have a complete equation, to cover changes in both current and reluctance and can apply it to energy and force problems.

Expressions for magnetic energy transfers

From Eqn(2.8), power transfer is given by $P = VI$. Integrating this to express energy change in terms of applied p.d. and current:

Energy transfer $W = \int VI\mathrm{d}t$ (9.3)

We now take Eqn(9.2), change its sign to indicate that we are dealing not with an induced e.m.f. but with the V applied to counteract it and cancel dt on the assumption that only smooth changes will be considered:

$$W = \int (LI\mathrm{d}I + I^2\mathrm{d}L) \tag{9.4}$$

This is the external energy change equation. It can be applied immediately to fixed linear inductors, for which only the first term exists and L can come outside the integral sign. Considering current increasing from zero to I:

$$W = L \int_0^I I\mathrm{d}I = LI^2/2 \tag{9.5}$$

Compare with $CV^2/2$ for the energy stored in a capacitor. For a change from I_1 to I_2, W would be equal to $L(I_1{}^2 - I_2{}^2)/2$. Carter, chapter 6, shows that energy methods can be used to estimate inductance, in a similar way to his methods for capacitance mentioned earlier.

As W is the energy supplied to the inductor to build the current up to I, and there is no sink of energy, $LI^2/2$ must also represent the energy stored in the inductor when passing a current I.

As in the electrostatic case, we can ask where the energy is stored, and we shall arrive at an expression showing that the field itself contains the energy, which can be described in terms of either or both of H and B. As a halfway stage, we will find the energy in a form which fits the magnetic circuit inside the inductor, so it can be applied to any magnetic circuit.

From the simple expression of Faraday's law with the sign changed to consider an applied p.d. rather than a back e.m.f.:

$$W = \int VI\mathrm{d}t = \int NI\mathrm{d}\Phi \tag{9.6}$$
$$= \int S\Phi\mathrm{d}\Phi \tag{9.7}$$
$$= S\Phi^2/2 \qquad \text{when } S \text{ is independent of } \Phi \tag{9.8}$$

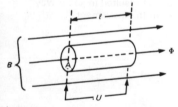

We assume B is parallel to H and have chosen the cylinder to be oriented as shown. δ quantities have been avoided, because confusion is likely between $\delta\Phi = B\delta A$ and $\delta\Phi$ produced by B changing, which is our concern here.

If B is not in the same direction as H, Eqn(9.9) must be written as $\int H.\mathrm{d}B$.

Compare Eqn(5.9) in electrostatics.

These equations represent the energy stored within a magnetic circuit, Eqns(9.7) and (9.8) being entirely in terms of internal quantities.

We consider now the energy stored in a small part of a magnetic circuit, replacing m.m.f. $\mathcal{M}$ or NI by m.s.p.d. U. Applying Eqn(9.6) to this small region, using Eqns(7.3) and 7.9) and allowing B to vary:

$$W = \int U\mathrm{d}\Phi$$
$$= \int Hl A\mathrm{d}B$$
$$= \int H\mathrm{d}B v \qquad \text{where } v \text{ is the volume} \tag{9.9}$$

$\int H\mathrm{d}B$ therefore represents the energy stored per unit volume within a magnetic circuit. For a linear material this is simply equal to:

$$W = \int \mu_0\mu_r H\mathrm{d}H$$
$$= \mu_0\mu_r H^2/2 \qquad \text{per unit volume} \tag{9.10}$$

As point quantities B and H are involved, the energy may be regarded as being stored in space, within the field itself.

Exercise 9.1   Calculate the energy stored in the iron and in the air gap in the broken toroid from Worked Example 7.1, for a current of 2 A. Assume that the iron behaves linearly and check by calculating the total energy using $LI^2/2$.
(Answer: energy in iron = 0.1 J; in air = 0.67 J; total = 0.77 J)

Hysteresis losses

If a magnetic field is established, the energy W to set it up has now been shown to be $\int H \mathrm{d}B$ per unit volume. On a graph of B against H, this will be the area between the curve and the B axis.

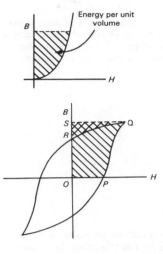

For a reversible material, this energy is all reclaimable. On removing H the resulting decrease in flux could generate an e.m.f. and drive current to transfer all the stored energy.

If hysteresis occurs, only part of the energy can be reclaimed. The figure in the margin shows a typical loop. If the material has been already cycled into that loop, then to move from P to Q, the energy put in per unit volume is equal to $\int H \mathrm{d}B$, which is the area $OPQS$ for that operation. On removing H, some energy could be recovered as explained above, equal to the area RSQ. The area $OPQR$ thus represents the energy per unit volume lost during this quadrant of the curve. Using a similar argument on the rest of the loop, it should be clear that the area of the whole loop is the energy lost per unit volume per cycle. Hence the use of materials with a small loop for the cores of electromagnetic machinery.

Reluctance force

Using the same principle as we used earlier in electrostatics, that
force = – d(potential energy)/dx
we can now determine forces in magnetic systems. Force produced entirely from energy changes due to varying reluctance can be called **reluctance force**. As an example, if a piece of iron is held just outside the end of a coil through which a current flows, a force on the iron is felt. If the reluctance can be determined in terms of the position of the iron, then in principle the force can be found at all points. This is not often easy, unless the problem is made artificially straightforward by assuming parallel flux lines.

Eqn(9.6) can be applied to the sliding wire arrangement in Fig. 7.2, to show that $F = BI\ell$ is consistent with $F = -\mathrm{d}W/\mathrm{d}x$.

Figure 9.1 shows an actuator for operating the magnetic tape drive mechanism in a computer, which is to provide a force of 4 N when the sliding bar is in the rest position with x equal to 2 mm. Determine the number of turns required in the coil if an operating current of 1.5 A is available. The length of each arm Pp or Qq of the

Worked Example 9.1

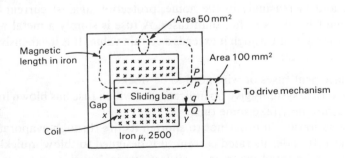

Fig. 9.1   Electromagnetic actuator for Worked Example 9.1.

magnetic circuit in iron is approximately 80 mm and the sliding fit air gaps at Pp and Qq are effectively 0.025 mm.

Solution: The magnetic circuit consists of two arms in parallel, each one made up of 80 mm iron and $(x + 0.025)$ mm air and of cross-section 50 mm². The flux must be found in terms of x, hence the energy and, by differentiating, the force. Current I will appear as an unknown all through, to be found when the required force is substituted at $x = 2$ mm. Now:

The sliding bar is of double the area, so effectively the circuit is two arms in parallel with the same uniform cross-section.

$$F = - \frac{\mathrm{d}W}{\mathrm{d}x} = - \frac{\mathrm{d}W}{\mathrm{d}\Phi} \times \frac{\mathrm{d}\Phi}{\mathrm{d}x}$$

From Eqn(9.6) $\mathrm{d}W/\mathrm{d}\Phi = NI$, so only $\mathrm{d}\Phi/\mathrm{d}x$ needs now to be found.

Calling the sliding fit air gaps y, then from Eqn(6.5) the reluctance S for each of the two flux paths is given by:

$$S = \frac{1}{\mu_0 A} \left(\frac{l}{\mu_r} + y + x \right)$$

So $\Phi = 2NI/S = 2NI \left| \dfrac{1}{\mu_0 A} \left(\dfrac{l}{\mu_r} + y + x \right) \right.$ as there are two parallel paths

x must not be made equal to 2 mm at this point, because it is the variation in potential energy caused by x changing that provides the force. x remains a variable up to the last minute, therefore.

$$\mathrm{d}\Phi/\mathrm{d}x = - 2NI \left| \frac{1}{\mu_0 A} \left(\frac{l}{\mu_r} + y + x \right)^2 \right.$$

$$F = - NI \times \frac{\mathrm{d}\Phi}{\mathrm{d}x} = 2N^2 I^2 \left| \frac{1}{\mu_0 A} \left(\frac{l}{\mu_r} + y + x \right)^2 \right.$$

$$\text{so} \quad N = \frac{1}{I} \sqrt{\left[\frac{F}{2\mu_0 A} \left(\frac{l}{\mu_r} + y + x \right)^2 \right]}$$

Even with x only a few millimetres, the variable air gap makes up the major part of the reluctance.

   It is possible to fit this number in comfortably using 0.56 mm (24 s.w.g.) wire, which can carry 1.5 A without undue heating over the short time the actuator would be working.

Inserting numbers:

$$N = \frac{1}{1.5} \sqrt{\left[\frac{4}{2 \times 4\pi \times 10^{-7} \times 50 \times 10^{-6}} \left(\frac{0.08}{2500} + 2.5 \times 10^{-5} + 0.002 \right)^2 \right]}$$

$? \lambda = $ 295 turns $?$ $N = \underline{245}$

Exercise 9.2   Scale the actuator in Worked Example 9.1 up by 3 times linearly, use a current of (9×1.5) A in the same number of turns and find the force produced with x having a value of 6 mm. This should give you a feel for the scaling effects discussed in Chapter 8.
(Answer: Force = 325 N)

Electromagnetic circuit breakers

In industry and increasingly in the home, protection against current overloads relies on circuit breakers rather than fuses. A fuse is simply a metal wire which melts when the current through it exceeds a certain value. It is inexpensive, but has several disadvantages:

(a) Replacement fuses or wire need to be stocked.
(b) Inexpensive systems give no indication of which fuse has blown in a box, so correction may take some time.
(c) Most seriously, in order not to shorten its life through evaporation when run at just under its rated current, it is designed to 'blow' quickly at some ten times its rated value and will last several hours at currents only just above. It will not protect against a slight overload, therefore, which could

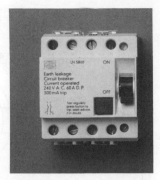

Fig. 9.2   Miniature and residual current circuit breakers (courtesy MK Electric Ltd, Edmonton, London).

nevertheless cause overheating elsewhere and perhaps start a fire or damage expensive parts of a circuit.

A direct electromagnetic circuit breaker, as illustrated in Fig. 9.2(a), is a spring-loaded switch that can be operated manually. When switched on, against the spring, a lock holds the mechanism in place. The device contains also an actuator, working on the principle of Worked Example 9.1. When a current in excess of the rated value passes through the actuator coil, the sliding rod releases a locking mechanism on the switch, which flies off. The breaker can only be switched back on manually, and then only if a current less than the rated value would be passed. The reader should check that all the disadvantages of fuses are overcome. The only advantage remaining to fuses, apart from initial cost, is that the same fuseholder can hold several alternative fuses, whereas circuit breakers are made for one current value only.

Figure 9.2(b) shows another important type of circuit breaker, again being used increasingly in the home. In this case the switch is operated if the difference in current between the live and neutral wires entering the circuit exceeds a set amount, and is for this reason called a residual current circuit breaker (RCCB). The reason for this difference would be a fault of some sort, causing current to flow to earth instead of along the return wire, either directly because of a short-circuit, as in Fig. 9.3(a), or through a person touching the live wire. In the latter case, Fig. 9.3(b) shows that the damage would be minimal if a 30 mA RCCB is used.

Reluctance minimization and field shapes

In the actuator example above, the force was in such a direction as to minimize x, and so minimize also the reluctance.

This is of general application, which can be seen easily at least for situations where motion is slow or has yet to start. In these cases any induced e.m.f. will be near zero, so from Eqn(6.1) the flux must be constant. Eqn(9.7) shows that if Φ is constant, magnetic potential energy is proportional to reluctance S. Systems in general tend to reduce their potential energy and thus any changes taking place will be in such a direction as to reduce reluctance also.

This could be written mathematically as:

Circuit breakers for use within small electronic circuits are usually thermally tripped rather than electromagnetically, because of the scaling problem with small sizes.

Though there is no reason why a multiple-tapped coil could not be used, with the switch coupled to a rotating label showing the rating corresponding to each position.

The RCCB is often called an Earth Leakage Circuit Breaker (ELCB) or Earth Leakage Trip (ELT), which describes its most common application.

In domestic systems, switches are in the live side only. During repairs, neutral can be accidentally shorted to earth and operate the RCCB even though no danger is involved. The author has been known to plunge his house into darkness from this cause!

For a fuller account of mains electrical safety techniques, and certainly before attempting any rewiring, consult the IEE *Wiring Regulations*.

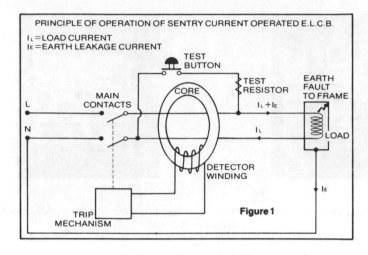

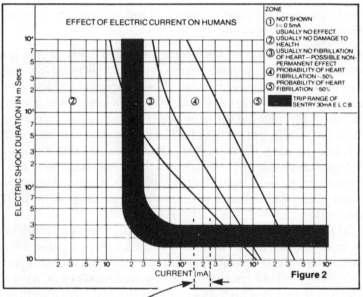

Fig. 9.3   Principles and safety margins for RCCBs (courtesy MK Electric Ltd).

$$S = NI/\Phi = \frac{\int \mathbf{H}.\mathbf{dl}}{\iint \mathbf{B}.\mathbf{dA}} \qquad \text{tends to a minimum value} \qquad (9.11)$$

Not only does this enable the direction of magnetic forces to be determined intuitively, but other aspects of magnetism can be understood in a useful way. Some examples follow, but the list is by no means exhaustive:

(a) The path occupied by magnetic flux in a gap will take the path of least reluctance. For the electromagnet poles in Fig. 9.4 it will follow path *b* rather than *a*, for which $\iint \mathbf{B}.\mathbf{dA}$ is too small, or *c* for which $\int \mathbf{H}.\mathbf{dl}$ is too big.

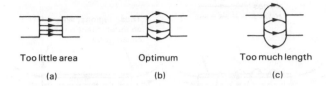

Too little area   Optimum   Too much length

(a)   (b)   (c)

Fig. 9.4   Flux paths for minimum reluctance across a gap.

(b) If magnetic material is placed in a field, flux lines will take the path of least reluctance, through the material, rather than follow a path through the air. Permeable materials can be considered to 'conduct' flux. This allows the magnetic screening of instruments by enclosing them in a container made of high permeability material.

(c) Record/playback heads for use in audio, video and computer systems work by allowing a magnetic medium to 'conduct' flux from a shaped gap, as shown in Fig. 9.5.

In Chapter 6 the use of an additional gap for linearization was discussed. This need should be even clearer now you can see how variable the 'front gap' will be, depending as it does on contact between surface and head and on the properties of the recording medium.

Permanent Magnets

Permanent magnets have been mentioned already in connection with hysteresis loops and materials in Chapter 8, and it should be clear that a large area loop is required. It may be thought that the B field left within a permanent magnet after full magnetization is simply the retentivity, but this turns out to be true only if the material is in the form of a continuous ring, in which case the field cannot be used!

To see why a useful magnet, with an incomplete material circuit, does not produce a field of ideal strength, consider Ampere's law, Eqn(7.10), which is $\oint H.dl$ = $\Sigma\ NI$. For a permanent magnet there is no current as it has been switched off. Therefore $\oint H.dl$ must be zero. In the space around the magnet, the field is

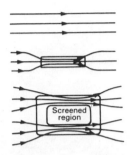

Carter, chapter 5, shows how the screening efficiency can be calculated and gives a general method for estimating the shape of fields near permeable materials.

If only recording signal were applied to the head, just the region near the origin of the B–H curve would be used. This is of relatively gentle gradient and markedly non-linear. A bias signal, well above audio frequency, is added to the signal to be recorded, to make the tape operate in a loop considerably greater than this:

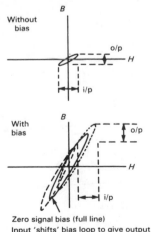

Zero signal bias (full line)
Input 'shifts' bias loop to give output

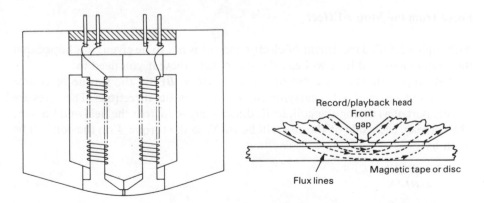

Fig. 9.5   Flux paths in tape or disc recording (audio recording head courtesy Magnetic Components Ltd, Chertsey, Surrey).

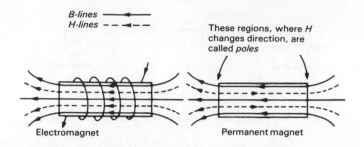

B-lines ——— ◄——
H-lines – – ◄ – –

These regions, where H changes direction, are called *poles*

Electromagnet   Permanent magnet

Fig. 9.6 B and H fields in an electromagnet and a permanent magnet.

indistinguishable from that of an electromagnet, for which $\int H.dl$ most definitely has a value. The H field outside the permanent magnet must be similar, which is in the direction of the B field and related to it numerically by $B = \mu_0 H$. To make the loop integral zero, the H field inside the magnet must be in the opposite direction to B, as shown in Fig. 9.6. The B field loops must be continuous, as flux is conserved under all conditions, including in the presence of magnets.

Thus within the magnetic material, the H field and B field correspond to the second quadrant of the hysteresis loop. The shape of the magnet will determine exactly where on the loop the magnet will operate. Ampere's law for the magnet can be written as:

$$\int (H.dl)_{\text{magnet}} = -\int (H.dl)_{\text{air}}$$

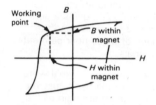

The shorter the passage in air relative to material, therefore, the stronger will be the H field in air but the weaker will it be in the material. So a horseshoe magnet will produce a much stronger field than will a bar magnet even if both followed their saturation loops when made. Moreover, the horseshoe magnet will be operating at a point nearer the B axis, as its internal H field will be less, so external fields will have less demagnetizing influence. For storage, putting a 'keeper' across the ends of the horseshoe magnet, or packing bar magnets side by side with opposite poles in contact, reduces the internal H field to zero, allowing the magnetization to remain indefinitely in the absence of very strong applied fields.

Carter, chapter 5, takes these ideas further.

Force from the Motor Effect

Although a detailed treatment of electric motors is not to be given, it is hoped that the foundations laid here will enable you to learn these if you need to.

Most applications of the motor law $F = I(l \times B)$ use the torque or couple produced in a pair of wires carrying currents in opposite directions. The wires are usually part of a rectangular coil; let its dimensions be l across the field and b along. The force on each side of the coil will be $BIlN$, so the torque T on the coil will be given by:

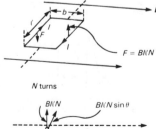

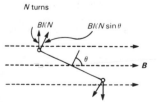

$$\begin{aligned} T &= BIlNb \\ &= BIAN \end{aligned} \qquad (9.12)$$

where A is the area of the coil. As any shape can be considered as being made up from rectangles, and torques merely add, Eqn(9.12) will apply to a flat coil of any shape with its axis normal to a uniform field. If the axis of the coil is at an angle θ to the field, the force for the torque will be supplied by the component of $BIlN$ at right angles to the plane of the coil, which is $BIlN \sin \theta$. So in general:

$$T = BIAN \sin \theta \qquad (9.13)$$

The torque can be described using the cross-product of vectors as $T = IN(A \times B)$. It is left to the reader to verify this by applying the right-hand rule and some lateral thinking.

The moving-coil meter

An application of torque on a coil is to be found in the familiar moving-coil meter movement. This is less accurate but still marginally cheaper than its digital counterpart, and is at present able to follow more rapid changes and show trends more readily.

For a linear movement, with the coil torque balanced by a linear hairspring or torsion wire, the torque should be directly proportional to the current. The sine factor in Eqn(9.13) must be removed, therefore. This is usually accomplished by tailoring the field in the region of the coil so that whatever the coil position, flux lines cross it in the coil plane, at an angle θ of zero.

For a more detailed account see Bennett, chapter 8.

Moving-coil loudspeaker

The coil in a loudspeaker needs to produce the same backwards and forwards movement as the diaphragm in the electrostatic speaker discussed in Chapter 5. A purely radial field is needed, set up by a permanent magnet as shown in Fig. 9.7.

Current in the coil is at all times across the field, resulting in a force either out of or further into the cylindrical channel. This force is transmitted to the paper or plastic cone, which couples the motion to the air.

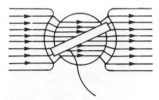

This is another example of a system minimizing its reluctance. Most of the reluctance in the magnetic circuit is in the air gap. To minimize reluctance, the gap must be crossed by the shortest path, as shown.

Definition of the ampere

The force on a wire in a B field is given by Eqn(7.2) and is proportional to the current in the wire and the field. But the field itself can be made dependent on another current, so the force between two wires can be expressed in terms only of currents, geometry and μ_0.

Show that the force per metre F_m between two wires, long compared with their separation x, and carrying currents I_1 and I_2, is given by $F_m = \mu_0 I_1 I_2 / 2\pi x$.

Exercise 9.3

This is used in defining μ_0 and the ampere as follows. If the wires in Exercise 9.3 are separated by 1 m and the same current passing through each produces a force of

Long straight wires are clearly inconvenient shapes for experimental arrangements, but equations can be set up for more realistic configurations. Apparatus exists, at the National Physical Laboratory for instance, which can calibrate a meter using an ampere defined entirely from force measurements. See, for example, Bennett, chapter 1, for details.

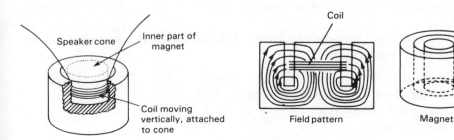

Fig. 9.7 Electromagnetic loudspeaker operation.

2×10^{-7} N between them, a current of 1 A is said to be passing. This requires μ_0 to be defined as equal to $4\pi \times 10^{-7}$ H m^{-1}.

Summary

For a system where both I and L can change, the induced e.m.f. is given by:

$$\mathcal{E} = -\frac{L\,dI}{dt} - \frac{I\,dL}{dt}$$

Energy transfer W can be variously written as:

$$W = \int L\,dI + I^2\,dL = \int NI\,d\Phi = \int S\Phi\,d\Phi = \int H\,dBv$$

Energy lost per unit volume per cycle, for a material undergoing a hysteresis loop, is equal to the area of the loop.

Reluctance force $= dW/dx$ where W includes a variable x that delineates a reluctance change.

Direct circuit breakers open a switch when their rated current is exceeded.

Residual current circuit breakers carry out a similar operation when the currents in two wires differ by more than a set amount.

Systems tend to minimize their reluctance. This idea aids understanding of field shapes between electromagnet poles, in screening and in magnetic recording.

For a permanent magnet, Ampere's law gives:

$$\int (H.dl)_{\text{magnet}} = - \int (H.dl)_{\text{air}}$$

showing a demagnetizing field exists in the magnet. Its strength depends on the shape of the magnet.

Torque on a flat coil in a field is given by $T = BIAN$ sine θ.

The ampere can be defined from the force between two wires.

Problems

*Indicates a more challenging problem.

Note this is a $\Phi - \mathcal{M}$ plot, not a $B - H$ plot.

9.1 In a hysteresis test on a transformer core, a plot of the loop is obtained on axes of total flux against m.m.f. and such that on the vertical scale 10 squares represents 200 μWb, on the horizontal 10 squares represents 250 A. The total loop area is found to be 3000 squares. Calculate the hysteresis power loss at 50 Hz.

9.2 Find the force between the poles of a horseshoe electromagnet of the following design:

Number of turns	: 400
Current, from constant voltage supply	: 10 A
Cross-section of air gap	: 6.4×10^{-3} m^2
Air gap length	: 10 mm

Assume the reluctance of the core is negligible and flux is parallel across the gap.

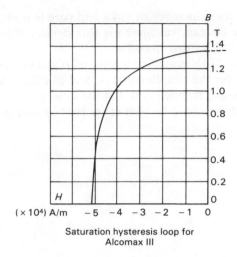

Saturation hysteresis loop for
Alcomax III

Fig. 9.8   2nd quadrant of $B - H$ curve for Problem 9.3.

*9.3 A permanent magnet in the shape of a broken ring is to be made, using material shaped into a rod 200 mm long × 10 mm diameter whose saturation hysteresis loop has a second quadrant as shown in Fig. 9.8.

Assuming the flux lines within both ring and gap can be regarded as evenly spaced and parallel, calculate the gap width that will produce the maximum energy density ($\propto HB$). You will need to plot a graph of HB against H, from the data given.

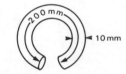

Carter, chapter 5, includes a justification of the maximum BH criterion.

9.4 Figure 9.9(a) shows a design for a moving-coil wattmeter.

The current to be measured passes through coil A, which has 110 turns and a resistance of 0.12Ω.

The voltage to be measured is applied across a series circuit consisting of coil B and a resistor, of total resistance 120 kΩ. Coil B has 180 turns and the torque it experiences is opposed by a hairspring.

(a) Ignoring end-effects, calculate the reluctance of the total air gap to flux generated by coil A, if the gap dimensions are as shown in Fig. 9.9(b).

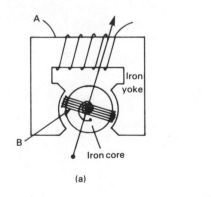

(a)

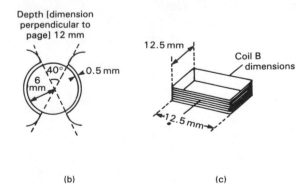

(b)   (c)

Fig. 9.9   Moving-coil wattmeter design for Problem 9.4.

(b) Assuming the reluctance of yoke and core is negligible compared with that of the air gap, calculate the flux density B in the air gap when a current of 0.6 A flows in coil A.

(c) A voltage of 230 V is applied across coil B and the series resistor. Refer to Fig. 9.9(c) for the coil dimensions, and calculate the torque on it when 0.6 A is passing through coil A at the same time.

(Hatfield Polytechnic 1st year exam 1984 — part question)

Electromagnetism and Charged 10
Particles

Objectives

☐ To find an expression for the force on a charged particle in a combination of electric and magnetic fields.

☐ To introduce the Hall effect, where such particles are contained in a solid, derive equations for it and consider some of its applications.

☐ To introduce the principles and enumerate the methods of removing electrons from a solid.

☐ To describe an electrode structure that would accelerate electrons to a set speed.

☐ To show how electric and magnetic fields are used for both deflection and focusing of electron streams.

☐ To describe the principles of display and camera tubes and image intensifiers.

The Lorentz Force

In this chapter we look at the way a charged atomic particle, such as an electron, moves under the combined influence of electrostatic and magnetic fields.

The electric force F_e on a particle of charge q due to an electric field E is given by $F_e = qE$. Similarly, the magnetic force F_m on such a particle moving at velocity v is given by $F_m = q(v \times B)$.

If the electric and magnetic fields are regarded as independent, the two forces will add as vectors, to give:

$$F = q[E + (v \times B)] \tag{10.1}$$

The force described in this way is called the **Lorentz force**.

When the charged particle is an electron or other atomic particle, the two most important engineering applications of the equation are concerned with particles moving in a solid, the Hall effect, and with streams of particles moving in a vacuum.

This is for historical reasons connected with the development of ideas leading up to the theory of Relativity. H.A. Lorentz (1853 – 1928) was closely involved with this work.

The Hall Effect

In Chapter 7, the motor and dynamo effects were shown to be just two different aspects of the motion of charged particles in a thin rod. Electrical energy could be turned into mechanical or vice versa.

Now consider what happens if the electric and magnetic fields are applied not across a thin rod but to a slice of material as in Fig. 10.1(a). The particles will move as before, but this time as well as applying a force to the slice, the motion will cause

Although this force can be measured, it is not usually significant.

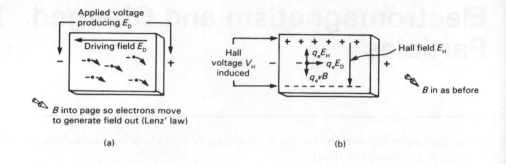

Fig. 10.1   Hall effect with negative charge carriers.

Ritchie, chapter 1, explains majority and minority carriers.

charge to pile up noticeably on one side of it. An induced p.d. will therefore be generated without any motion of the slice itself to cause it. This is the Hall effect.

As an example, consider a material such as an n-type semiconductor, in which electrons are the main or majority charge carriers, of charge q_e. At the instant of switching on the fields, which in Fig. 10.1(a) are E from right to left, B into the page, the electrons will move in curved paths as shown.

The actual shape of the electron paths is not easy to determine, but in most cases the detailed motion on first switching on the fields is unimportant, as equilibrium is established on a time-scale much smaller than a microsecond.

Because of the resulting drift downwards on the diagram, the bottom of the slice becomes negative and, by depletion, the top positive, setting up an electric field, the Hall field E_H, across the slice. This will apply an upward force $q_e E_H$ to each electron, counteracting the magnetically produced force. As more electrons move down, a stronger Hall field is produced until eventually an equilibrium is established and the vertical component of the Lorentz force is zero as shown in Fig. 10.1(b).

If the majority carriers are not electrons but positive holes, the deflection is the same way, as Fig. 10.2 shows.

Such a material is called an intrinsic semiconductor. In practice a small Hall voltage would be produced because of the differing mobilities of electrons and holes.

Thus the polarity of the Hall voltage shows immediately whether the majority carrier population consists of electrons or holes. A Hall voltage of zero would suggest approximately equal concentrations of electrons and holes. These important conclusions are often used in semiconductor research, as will be described later.

Fig. 10.2   Hall effect with positive charge carriers.

Equations for the Hall effect

In order to relate the electric fields to the driving and Hall voltages, we need to know the dimensions of the slice. Figure 10.3 shows these and all the other variables involved.

In Chapters 2 and 3 the equations for charge flow were developed. These can be applied to Fig. 10.3 as follows:

Eqn(2.5), $I = nAqv$, leads to $\qquad I_D = nbdq_e v$ $\qquad\qquad$ (10.2)

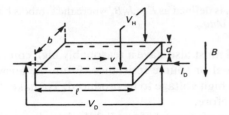

Fig. 10.3   Variables for Hall effect equations.

Eqn(2.12), $V/I = l/\sigma A$, leads to $V_D/I_D = l/\sigma bd$ (10.3)

Eqn(3.7), $\mu = v/E$, leads to $\mu = vl/V_D$ (10.4)

Finally, we add the equation for field equilibrium, when the Lorentz force is zero at right angles to E_D. Writing magnitudes only:

$$q_eE_H = q_evB \qquad \text{so} \qquad V_H/b = vB \qquad (10.5)$$

These four equations can be combined as needed for a particular problem, whether to determine the charge mobility of a semiconductor material or to design a device in which the Hall effect is to be applied.

Resist the temptation to learn many other equations for the Hall effect; there is no unique set of 'Hall effect equations'. You are better off knowing the basic charge flow equations and being able to apply them to a Hall slice as described above.

Worked Example 10.1

In a Hall effect experiment, with a silicon slice 5 mm × 5 mm × 0.5 mm, oriented as in Fig. 10.3, a current of 10 mA in a magnetic field of strength 0.1 T produced a Hall voltage of 12.5 mV. The driving voltage across the slice was measured as 0.93 V. Calculate the carrier concentration and charge mobility for the specimen.

The charge on the electron is 1.6×10^{-19} C.

Solution: In this case, no single equation from the group can be applied immediately, so v will need to be eliminated as it is not required. See Fig. 10.3 for diagram and symbols.

Combining Eqns (10.2) and (10.5): $n = I_DB/dq_eV_H$

With the numbers in the question, $n = \dfrac{0.1 \times 0.1}{0.0005 \times 1.6 \times 10^{-19} \times 0.0125}$

Carrier concentration $n = 10^{22}$ m^{-3}

Combining Eqns (10.4) and (10.5):

$$\mu = V_Hl/bBV_D$$
$$= \frac{0.0125 \times 0.005}{0.005 \times 0.1 \times 0.93}$$

Charge mobility $\mu = 0.134$ m^2 V^{-1} s^{-1}

Hall effect materials

Any conductor will generate a Hall voltage, though some are markedly better than others. In general, a useful Hall material needs to generate as high a voltage as possible for a given value of driving current density and B field.

Exercise 10.1 The Hall coefficient R_H is defined as $E_H/J_D B$, where the symbols have the usual meanings. Show that it is equal to l/nq_e.

An effective material must also have a reasonably high conductivity to ensure the slice has a low internal or source resistance. From the answer to Exercise 10.1, n must be small for a high voltage to be produced. To make the conductivity high, μ must be large, therefore.

As $\sigma = nq_e\mu$.

Hall effect slices are often made from lightly doped materials of high mobility. Indium antimonide (InSb) is favoured, having an exceptionally high μ value.

Applications of the Hall Effect

Semiconductor research

As was explained earlier, the polarity of the Hall voltage can be used to determine the sign of the majority carriers in the slice material and their mobility. The Hall effect is, in fact, the only straightforward method of obtaining these important pieces of information.

For example $\mu = V_H\ell/BbV_D$. It is left to the reader to find equations from which v and n can be obtained.

Moreover, the equations developed above can be arranged so that the microscopic quantities v, μ and n are determined from purely macroscopic, or large scale, measurements, combined with an assumed value for q_e, the electron charge.

An example of this is research connected with the vacuum deposition of thin semiconductor films, where evaporated material is deposited on a substrate under ultra-high vacuum conditions. An immediate knowledge of μ and n is so useful that often the film is deposited through a mask which gives it a shape suitable for Hall effect measurements. In a few experimental rigs these can be carried out by moving the deposited film into a strong magnetic field while still within the vacuum chamber. Figure 10.4 shows the substrate in position ready for deposition through the mask, and the substrate after deposition, along with previously evaporated metal films to act as electrical contacts.

Mobility measurements carried out in this way have been particularly useful in following the effects of annealing and in finding what happens when such films are exposed to gases introduced into the vacuum chamber.

A current can be passed between A and F and the voltages measured at the other terminals. The mean driving voltage across the centre of the film is equal to (average of B and C – average of D and E) and the mean Hall voltage for the same region is given by (average of B and D – average of C and E). The film dimensions b and l on Fig. 10.3 are obtained from the mask measurements, and d can be obtained by using an electron microscope after the film has been removed from the vacuum chamber.

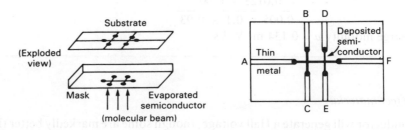

Fig. 10.4 Vacuum deposition allowing Hall effect measurements.

122

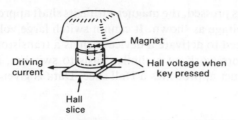

Fig. 10.5   Design for simple Hall effect key switch.

In an experiment reported by Williams and Parker, lead telluride was evaporated through a mask as discussed above to a thickness of 50 nm. The region of semiconductor under test was breadth 2mm × length 10 mm. With a driving current of 0.1 mA and a field of 30 mT, measurements gave for one sample a μ of 0.16 m^2 V^{-1}s^{-1} and n of 10^{24}. To enable another worker to set up suitable measuring equipment to check these readings, calculate the driving and Hall voltages that must have been measured in the original experiments.
(Answer: $V_D = 0.39$ V; $V_H = 0.375$ mV)

Exercise 10.2

Switches and proximity detectors

Mechanical switches suffer from three main defects:

(a)   Bounce, causing multiple triggering in logic circuits, and noise generally.
(b)   Wear, giving them a limited lifetime, perhaps up to 10^5 operations for an inexpensive example, which is inadequate for robot and keyboard uses.
(c)   Sparking, when used to switch inductive circuits while current is flowing. This can shorten the switch life and act as a fire hazard.

The Hall effect can be used to make a switch that overcomes all these problems, though at the price of a limited performance in other respects. The principle is straightforward, as Fig. 10.5 shows.

The letter E on a keyboard attached to a word processor in continuous use during office hours is hit on average perhaps once every 10 s. In that case it will be used 3/4 of a million times in one year!

hall effect i.c. switch ●

W. 4·52
H. 4·48

L. 12
Dia. 4

marked face

1. Output
2. Common
3. Supply

A miniature semi-conductor proximity switch utilising the Hall effect to give 'bounce free' switching when influenced by a magnetic field. A magnet is supplied which allows switching at distances up to 4 mm. This may be increased if the Hall effect i.c. is mounted against a ferromagnetic surface. The device is magnetically unidirectional requiring the marked south pole of the magnet to face away from the magnetic centre indicated by the dimple, or alternatively the magnet may be positioned on the other side of the i.c. but in this instance the marked face of magnet should be towards the i.c. Ideal for use in logic circuits where 'bounce free' switching is necessary.
Equivalent to UGN3020T.

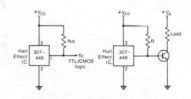

technical specification

Supply voltage	4·5 to 24 V
Supply current	6 mA at 24 V (no load)
I_{SINK} (max.)	20 mA
Magnetic flux density B	To operate 30 mT (35 mT max.)
	To release 16·5 mT (5 mT min.)
Output voltage	Low, 85 mV typ. (B ⩾ 35 mT)
	High, V_{CC} (B ⩽ 5 mT)
Output reverse current	High, 0·1 μA typ. (B ⩽ 5 mT)

Fig. 10.6   Hall effect proximity switch (courtesy RS Components Ltd).

When the switch is pressed, the magnet within its shaft approaches the Hall slice, setting up a Hall voltage as shown. It cannot switch large voltages or currents by itself, and would need to activate a device such as a transistor.

Proximity detectors work on a similar basis to switches, in that they give an output when a magnet approaches a Hall slice. Data is given in Fig. 10.6 on one commercial example.

Field, current and power measurement

With a coil, either B has to be changing or the coil must be moved to alter the flux through it. See Chapter 6.

As the Hall voltage is proportional to the applied B field, it can be used to measure it. The method has one clear advantage over a simple coil in that B is measureable even if constant.

There are two main disadvantages:

(a) Because the effect is fairly small, it cannot be used for very low fields as the voltages induced are then comparable to voltages generated by slight temperature differences across the slice, or are masked by interference. Fields of the order of 1 – 100 mT can be dealt with comfortably, but the earth's magnetic field of the order of a few tens of microteslas would be difficult to measure.

This means that some form of differential amplification may be necessary when used in a circuit. See Horowitz and Hill, chapter 7.

(b) A Hall probe would need calibration with known fields, as semiconductors cannot be tailored to exactly the required n and μ. It is also difficult to attach the contacts for driving current and Hall measurements exactly symmetrically.

The measurement of large currents via their magnetic fields is a growing application of Hall effect devices. As a magnetic field is external to the wire carrying the current, the circuit does not need to be broken to insert the ammeter. Any potential drop from the measurement can be made very small and actually zero for d.c.

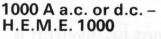

1000 A a.c. or d.c. – H.E.M.E. 1000

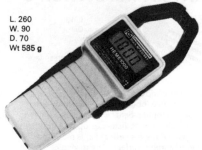

L. 260
W. 90
D. 70
Wt 585 g

Supplied to RS by H.E.M.E.
A clip-on ammeter utilising Hall-effect technology to measure current up to 1000 A at frequencies from d.c. to 1 kHz.

Conductor size   Up to 48 mm dia.
                              or 22×60 mm bus-bar.

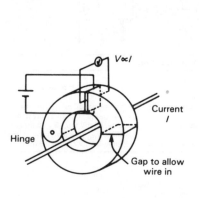

(a)

(b)

Fig. 10.7   Principle and example of a clamp meter (courtesy RS Components Ltd).

The principle is to surround the wire with a magnetic circuit containing a Hall effect device. The magnetic circuit is hinged and broken to allow it to be placed around the wire. By Ampere's law, the exact positioning is not critical. Such a system is called a **clip-on ammeter** or **clamp meter**. Figure 10.7 shows the principle and a commercial example.

As the Hall voltage is proportional to both magnetic field and driving current, a power meter can be made, to measure instantaneous (voltage × current). The current to be measured is passed through a coil which sets up the magnetic field. The Hall slice is part of the circuit, rather as in Fig. 10.7(a), and the driving current is derived from the voltage to be measured. The Hall voltage is thus proportional to the instantaneous (voltage × current).

It may be sensible to buffer the voltage to provide enough current to drive the slice. See Horowitz and Hill, chapter 3.

Electron Streams

For the remainder of this chapter we deal with the motion of electrons in a vacuum. They can achieve enormous speeds, very near to the speed of light, c, where their behaviour is controlled by the equations of special relativity. In most electronic applications, however, the maximum likely speed is only a few percent of c, so we shall not need to make any relativistic corrections.

The fractional error in ignoring relativity is $v^2/2c^2$, where v is the electron velocity, so if v is 5% of c, the error is 0.125%.

Production of free electrons above a solid

In Chapter 3, we discussed the production and acceleration of charged particles within a gas. We are dealing here with a vacuum, where any particles must be injected from a source, and we consider the particular examples where the source is solid and the particles electrons.

A quantity called the work function ϕ_w (phi) of a solid is defined as the energy required to remove an electron completely from its surface. This energy can be measured either in joules or in electron-volts (eV), where $1 \, \text{eV} = 1.6 \times 10^{-19} \, \text{J}$.

Electrons can be generated above a solid in four main ways:

(a) Field emission. A strong enough electric field, around $10^9 \, \text{V m}^{-1}$, can 'tear' electrons out of a metal.

(b) Photoelectric effect. Light travels as 'packets' of waves, called quanta, whose energy is proportional to the frequency of the light. The relationship is energy $W = hf$, where h is Planck's constant and f the frequency of the light. If the quantum energy of a particular frequency is greater than the work function of a metal, light of that frequency will cause electrons to be given off.

(c) Thermionic effect. If a solid is heated, the proportion of its electrons with energy greater than ϕ_w will increase until a noticeable quantity of them is released. This is accomplished either by pasing current through a metal such as tungsten to heat it to well over 1000°C or, more usually, by heating independently a metal tube covered with a mixture of oxides. The latter is more efficient and thus a lower temperature can be used.

(d) Secondary emission. Electrons travelling with a kinetic energy greater than the work function of a metal can knock other electrons out.

A small discharge tube can also act as a source, injecting ions into the vacuum chamber, as used in mass spectrometry. See, for instance, Caro, McDonell and Spicer, chapter 10.

The eV has the advantage that an external measurement of p.d. indicates straight away the energy in eV of any electrons or ions accelerated by that p.d. For most metals, ϕ_w is a few eV.

See Solymar and Walsh, chapter 6, for a description of this, involving the tunnel effect.

See Solymar and Walsh, chapter 2, for a detailed explanation of quanta. Free carrier generation in photoresistors, as described in Chapter 3, needs less energy as electrons are not being emitted into the space above the material.

There is a subtle difference between the effects of photons and of electrons when they strike a surface. Generally, photons liberate no more than 1 electron at a time, and any energy left over is given to the electron as kinetic energy. Energetic electrons do not lose their energy W_e at one blow, and can therefore knock out several, up to a maximum of W_e/ϕ_w. Even this is a simplified picture. See Solymar and Walsh, chapter 6, for more detail.

Acceleration of Electrons

As explained in Chapter 3, electrons moving through a potential difference ΔV undergo a kinetic energy change according to Eqn(3.15):

$$q_e\Delta V = mv^2/2$$

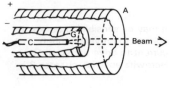

Electron gun

Carter, chapter 1, shows a more realistic design.

The marginal figure shows one design of electron 'gun'. The cathode C is a heated tube coated with oxide, emitting electrons thermionically as described above. G is at a negative potential, and therefore keeps any electrons in the space close to C. A is positive, relative to C, and will therefore accelerate electrons through the hole in G, at a sufficient rate that they are not diverted much, and so continue through the hole in A. A is usually at earth potential, so the beam travels freely into the rest of the system, screened from the high negative potentials inside the gun.

Logically it would seem sensible to deal with focusing next, as this would be the stage following acceleration in real electron optics, but deflection is considered because one of the techniques is used in a more subtle form for focusing.

Deflection and Focusing of Electron Streams

Electron deflection

Electron streams used in any kind of display device, such as a cathode ray oscilloscope or a TV display, will need deflecting in a controlled and preferably linear way. Two methods are available, one using electric and the other magnetic fields.

Electrostatic deflection

See any elementary mechanics or Physics book for a reminder of Newton's laws. Symbols are:

u initial velocity
v final velocity
a acceleration
t time
s displacement

It behaves like a projectile in a uniform gravitational field, therefore, and follows a parabolic path.

If an electron passes through a uniform electric field, its velocity normal to the field remains unchanged, while it will acccelerate uniformly along the field according to Newton's Second Law.

The field is made by parallel plates with the stream entering the field usually midway between the plates as in Fig. 10.8.

Ignoring edge effects, v_x is maintained, while v_y changes with distance according to $v^2 = u^2 + 2as$, where the symbols have the usual meanings. s in this case is the deflection achieved by the time t the stream reaches the end of the field. t can be calculated from the known speed v_x and the length l of the plates, and a from the field E and electron charge q_e and m_e.

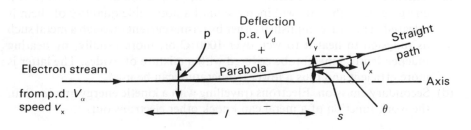

Fig. 10.8   Electrostatic beam deflection.

Find the angle of deflection of an electron stream accelerated through a potential difference of 5 kV and passing normal to the field between parallel plates and midway between them. The plates extend for 20 mm along the path of the electrons, are separated by 5 mm and have a p.d. of 150 V across them. Ignore edge effects and relativistic corrections.

Solution: Using Fig. 10.8 and symbols defined from it and the text below:

$$v_y = at \quad \text{where} \quad a = F/m = Eq/m = \frac{V_d q_e}{p m_e}$$

$t = l/v_x$ and v_x comes from $m_e v_x^2/2 = q_e V_a$

We require θ where $\tan \theta = v_y/v_x$.
Combining all these, $\theta = \arctan(V_d l / 2p V_a)$
Using the numbers supplied, $\theta = 3.4°$

Worked Example 10.2

Don't attempt to learn this final equation, simply ensure you understand how to obtain it and similar equations from the more basic ones. Note that m_e and q_e cancel, so this deflection would be the same for any charged particle.

This answer shows why cathode ray tubes for oscilloscopes tend to be long and thin, to achieve a reasonable linear deflection from such a small angle, and why TV tubes, using higher accelerating p.d.s and requiring much larger angular deflections, use magnetic techniques.

Magnetic deflection
In Chapter 7, the force on a charged particle in a magnetic field was derived and Eqn(7.6) $F = q(v \times B)$ was the result. As it is always at right angles to the particle path, the force is a centripetal one and in a uniform B field a circular path results, with no change in particle speed.

A centripetal force produces a path of radius R given by $F = mv^2/R$. The equation connecting all these quantities is thus $mv_n^2/R = qv_n B$ where v_n is the component of particle velocity normal to the magnetic field. Thus:

$$R = mv_n/qB \tag{10.6}$$

For an analysis of circular motion see any elementary Physics book.

Electrons from a 25 kV gun in a colour television receiver cross a magnetic field of strength 0.01 T occupying a circular region of radius 20 mm. Ignoring edge effects, determine the deflection angle.
Electron charge 1.6×10^{-19} C; mass 9.1×10^{-31} kg.

Solution: Referring to the marginal figure, the only complication is a geometrical one, connecting the radius R of the path with the deflection angle and radius r of the circle defining the field boundary.

It should be clear from the diagram that in the triangle *OAB*:

$\tan \theta/2 = r/R$
Using Eqn(10.6) $= rq_e B/m_e v$ where v comes from $m_e v^2/2 = q_e V$

Combining all these:

$\theta/2 = \arctan[rB\sqrt{(q_e/m_e V)}]$
With numbers, $\theta = 55.9°$

Worked Example 10.3

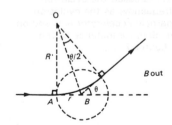

127

Electron focusing

The beam produced by an electron gun is usually diverging, and so needs focusing, so all the electrons will pass through the same point again somewhere in the system. Two out of several methods will be described, one electrostatic, the other magnetic.

Electrostatic focusing

An equally effective system has the nearer one at the lower potential! See Oatley, chapter 10.

One method uses a pair of coaxial cylinders, both at a positive potential but the one nearest the electron gun at a higher potential than the other, as in Fig. 10.9.

The electron path shown is diverging from the axis of the system. When an electron following this path reaches the field between the cylinders it is deflected even further away, as electrons move 'up' E lines. On entering the second cylinder, it is deflected towards the axis, again moving 'up' the lines. As it has also travelled from a more to a less positive region it has slowed down, so the second deflection will be larger than the first, returning the electron towards the axis. It will cross it at some point, ideally with electrons pursuing other paths. The calculations of field shape are very complex and are not dealt with here.

Numerical methods are usually necessary. Carter, chapter 1 gives details.

Magnetic focusing

Of the several techniques available, the easiest to understand has been chosen, which uses a magnetic field directed along the axis of the beam.

If all the electrons in the beam travelled parallel to the axis, the beam would, of course, be unaffected, but the beam from an electron gun spreads out. The electrons will have more or less the same axial component of velocity, but different transverse components. In the absence of a magnetic field, an observer looking along the axis would see electrons moving radially out away from the source. To be focused, they must move so as to cross the axis once more after a length of time which is the same for each electron. Because they move along the axis at the same speed, they will then cross all at the same place.

$$F = q(v \times B)$$
$$= qvB \sin \theta$$

If $\theta = 0$ so will be F

The circular path followed by an electron in a uniform magnetic field has one remarkable property: the time taken for a complete 'orbit' is independent of the electron speed. This can be seen from the following:

From Eqn(10.6) $R = mv_n/qB$

Time for one orbit $T = \text{distance/speed}$

                     $= 2\pi R/V_n = 2\pi mv_n/qBv_n$ from which v_n cancels.

$1/T$ is called the cyclotron frequency, as the cyclotron particle accelerator is based on it. See, for instance Duffin, chapter 7.

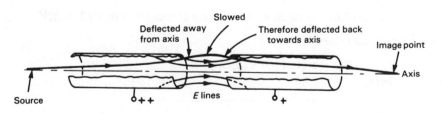

Fig. 10.9   Electrostatic beam focusing.

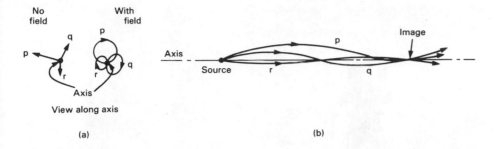

View along axis

(a)

(b)

Fig. 10.10   Axial magnetic beam focusing.

Thus the time is independent of both R and v_n. All electrons in a given field take exactly the same time to complete one orbit.

Returning to our axial beam, with the field applied the observer looking down the beam will see electrons following a circular path, leaving the source and all arriving back at a point on the axis after the same time as shown in Fig 10.10(a). If all electrons travel at the same axial speed, they all arrive back on the axis at the same point and are therefore focused, as in Fig. 10.10(b).

Calculate the axial field B required to focus electrons to a point 80 mm from a source hole, through which they emerge after being accelerated by a p.d. of 6 kV.
(Answer: $B = 20.5$ mT)

Exercise 10.3

A suitable axial field could be obtained by sending the beam down the axis of a long coil. This method is unsuitable for systems where the beam is required to be deflected so the electrostatic method is used in TV and cathode ray tubes.

If the beam were deflected it would follow a helical path and arrive back on the axis! Nevertheless, this system is used in some camera tube systems, by carefully tailoring the magnetic fields involved in focusing and scannii

Fig. 10.11   Oscilloscope c.r.t. (first published in Rees, D.T.: *The Cathode Ray Oscilloscope*; Longmans, by courtesy of the author and publisher).

Fig. 10.12   Electron gun end of VDU picture tube showing line scan coils and fine adjustment magnets (courtesy Thorn-EMI Brimar Ltd, Manchester).

Some Applications of Electron Streams

Cathode ray tubes (c.r.t.s)

C.R.T.s for oscilloscopes are relatively small and can be long compared with their width. An accelerating p.d. of only a few kilovolts is sufficient to give adequate brightness. The deflection can be by the simpler electrostatic method, therefore. Figure 10.11 shows a commercial example.

For television and visual display unit (V.D.U) use, a large screen area is needed and because the whole area is illuminated a very high brightness spot must be used. To avoid a large beam current the accelerating potential is made as high as possible without producing an X-ray hazard; about 20 kV is common. At the same time the tube must not be long compared with its width, for obvious reasons. A beam deflection of up to 70° each way is used, which with the high accelerating potential makes magnetic deflection essential. Figure 10.12 shows a typical V.D.U or TV tube.

All c.r.t.s have a limited frequency response due to the transit time of electrons through the deflection region. If an attempt is made to change the deflection angle too quickly, electrons still within the region will take on a combination of old and new deflections, so a distorted image or trace will be seen.

TV camera tubes

In the vidicon type of tube, shown in Fig. 10.13, a lens produces an image of a scene on a photoconductive target, which is connected to the input of an amplifier. An electron beam scans the target in synchronism with the beam in the TV tube receiving the picture. When the camera beam strikes a point on the target, a current flows into the amplifier input roughly proportional to the illumination of that point, because of the photoconduction. The intensity of the beam in the TV receiver can be made dependent on this current and thus proportional to the illumination of the corresponding point in the original scene.

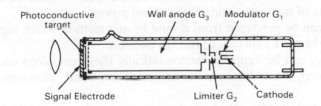

Fig. 10.13   Vidicon camera tube (courtesy Thorn EMI Electron Tubes Ltd, Ruislip, Middx)

Image intensifiers

Image intensifiers are used for night-time surveillance and to enhance the very faint images gathered by optical and infra red telescopes in astronomy.

As with the vidicon tube, an image of a scene is focused on a target, which is this time photoemissive, not photoconductive. Figure 10.14 shows an example.

Electrons are emitted into the space behind the target and accelerated by a field between the target and a phosphor screen. An axial focusing field is applied also, so

The author acknowledges that electron beam devices are being replaced gradually by solid-state imaging and display technology. It may well be that a future edition or replacement of this book will omit this section entirely, but while cathode ray and TV picture tubes are still in common use, an understanding of their operation and limitations is deemed useful.

The spot is so bright that if the scanning were to stop for even a short time the beam would burn a hole in the phosphor. Beam acceleration and scanning circuits are interlinked, therefore, as discussed in Problem 10.5.

Photoconductive materials were dealt with in detail earlier. Increased illumination reduces the resistance of such materials.

The proportionality is not exact, and 'gamma-correction' has to be provided in the amplifier to linearize the response. The explanation is incomplete also; for more details consult EEV, Chelmsford, Essex, or Thorn-EMI Electron Tubes Ltd, Ruislip, Middx, to both of whom the author is grateful for useful information received.

'Photoemissive' is used where formerly 'photoelectric' would have appeared. High-voltage rings are also placed within the sections for fine focusing. Details can be obtained from Thorn-EMI, to whom the author is grateful for information received.

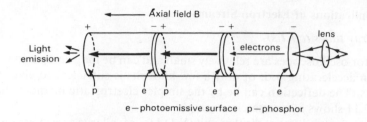

Fig. 10.14   3-Stage image intensifier tube design.

a new clear image is made on the screen, which can be up to 50 times brighter than the original. Intensifiers can be connected in cascade to produce further multiplications by 50; three such units are commonly used, as shown in the Figure.

As an alternative technique, a single tube is used with fine mesh metal screens inserted at intervals. Accelerated electrons generate further ones by secondary emission and these are again accelerated to produce a further multiplication.

There is a note earlier in the chapter on secondary emission. This is sometimes called the photomultiplier principle. See also Horowitz and Hill, chapter 14.

Summary

For a particle of charge q moving at velocity v in a region containing a magnetic field B and an electric field E, the Lorentz force F on it is given by:

$$F = q[E + (v \times B)]$$

In a slice of material containing charges driven across a magnetic field, those charges move to set up an electric field called the Hall field at right angles to their initial motion. Once equilibrium is established, the Lorentz force for other moving charges becomes zero.

The Hall field E is proportional to the magnetic field strength and driving current, and depends also on the dimensions of the slice.

Applications of the Hall effect include semiconductor research, switches and measurements of magnetic fields, current and power.

Electrons can be produced from a solid by any method which supplies energy greater than the work function ϕ_w to each electron.

Such energy can be supplied electrostatically (field emission) and from light (photoemission), heat (thermionic emission) or other electrons (secondary emission).

A system of electrodes called an electron gun can be set up which produces a slightly diverging beam of electrons, at a speed given by Eqn(3.15).

An electron stream can be deflected by an electric field, where it accelerates 'up' the E lines at a rate a given by Eq/m or by a magnetic field, where it takes up a circular path of radius R given by equating centripetal force mv^2/R with magnetic force qvB, where v is the component of velocity normal to B.

An electron stream can be focused by using the field between two axial cylinders or the fact that the orbit time for electrons in a B field is independent of their speed. Thus electrons with slightly off-axis directions in an otherwise constant speed flight down a B field are returned to the axis at a defined image point.

These principles can be applied to the display and collection of visual data, respectively in c.r.t.s and in camera tubes and image intensifiers.

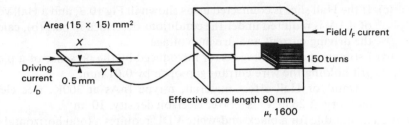

Fig. 10.15 Diagram for Problem 10.2.

Problems

*Indicates more challenging parts of problems.

Take electron charge q_e as 1.6×10^{-19} C and electron mass m_e as 9.1×10^{-31} kg.

10.1 Calculate the electric field required to reduce the Lorentz force on an electron to zero when it is in a magnetic field of strength 0.01 T and travelling at a speed of 8×10^6 ms^{-1}.

10.2 Figure 10.15 represents a Hall effect system for investigating semiconductor specimens.

    (a) For a field current I_F of 100 mA, calculate the magnetic field strength B through the specimen, assuming μ_r is 1 for the specimen, and ignoring fringe effects and flux leakage.

    (b) When 3 V is applied to drive current through the specimen, a current I_D of 24 mA is produced. With the field applied as in part (a), a Hall voltage of 12 mV is measured, X being positive relative to Y. Calculate the effective concentration and mobility of the carriers in the specimen, stating whether the material is p-type (mainly positive carriers) or n-type (mainly negative).

    (Hatfield Polytechnic 1st year examination 1981 — part question.)

10.3 Figure 10.16 represents a design for a clamp meter, using the Hall effect:

    (a) Use an average value of iron radius to estimate the reluctance of the iron to flux generated by a current in a wire through the central hole. Hence estimate the total reluctance of the magnetic circuit.

    (b) Taking your estimates from (a), and for a current of 100 A through the central hole, calculate an average value for B.

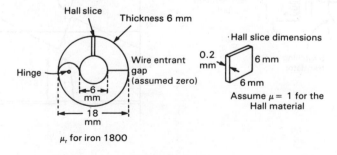

Fig. 10.16 Clamp meter for Problem 10.3.

133

(c) If the Hall slice is connected up as shown in Fig 10.3, and a Hall voltage of 0.1 V is required under the conditions described in part (b), calculate the driving current and driving voltage.

(d) Estimate the percentage error introduced by the presence of a piece of grit holding the wire entrant gap open by 0.01 mm.

Data for Hall effect material, n-type InAs at 300K: free electron mobility, $2.26 \text{ m}^2\text{V}^{-1}\text{s}^{-1}$; free electron density, 10^{21}m^{-3}.

10.4 A c.r.t. suitable for a black-and-white VDU requires a total horizontal beam deflection of 135°, using an accelerating p.d. of 16kV. The deflection must all take place within a region defined by a circle of diameter 40 mm.

(a) Show that electrostatic deflection would demand a wildly impractical deflection p.d.

(b) Find a value of B to provide full deflection either way.

(c) Find the current needed in two series coils, each of 100 turns, to provide this field on their axis, halfway between them. Treat them as flat coils, of 40 mm diameter separated by 20 mm.

See Fig. 10.17 for the rest of the question, in which resistive losses may be ignored.

(d) The current in part (c) must change from full positive to full negative in one line sweep, then back again during the 5 μs flyback period. The 16 kV accelerating p.d. can be generated during flyback in one secondary winding of a transformer, whose other secondary supplies the scan coils with current. Calculate the mutual inductance required between these windings in the transformer.

*(e) The d.c. supply in the VDU is 45 V, virtually all of which can appear across the transformer primary during the scan period. Calculate the mutual inductance between primary and scan secondary.

You will need to use the method of Problem 7.4. This is called the Helmholtz arrangement, and gives the most uniform field between two separate flat coils. See Duffin, chapter 7.

This means that if the scan dies, so does the electron beam, protecting the phosphor.

This is considerably simplified, but does illustrate the principles. Remember that once current is flowing in an inductor, a reverse p.d. is required to reduce it. The capacitor stores charge when the switch opens, while the current through the primary decays as the potential at C rises. The capacitor then discharges, sending current back into the supply and reducing the potential at C to zero. The diode prevents the potential going below zero and allows current to rise from its negative peak to repeat the process. The transistor is switched on while the current is negative.

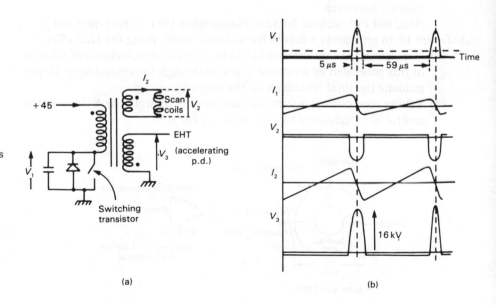

Fig. 10.17   EHT/scan transformer for Problem 10.5.

*(f) Make a rough calculation of the self-inductance of the scan coils and from your results so far, estimate the turns ratio primary: scan secondary: EHT secondary, assuming no losses.

11 The Electromagnetic Field

Objectives

Be warned that this chapter is in perhaps a more light-hearted vein than the previous ten. They have laid the foundations for serious study, but to pursue the concepts in this chapter fully will require greater mathematical facility than you are likely to possess at this stage. A book such as Carter will lead you from this point to greater depth. However, a useful intuitive appreciation of pulse speeds, characteristic impedance, electromagnetic waves and even special relativity can be gained from the work done so far in this book, so no apology is made for introducing these topics, albeit with less rigour and perhaps more arm-waving than has been the case in previous chapters.

□ To describe how the capacitance and inductance per unit length of a transmission line determine the speed of an electrical pulse.

□ To obtain an expression for pulse speed and characteristic impendance in a transmission line.

□ To show that pulse speed is independent of geometry and with no dielectric or magnetic materials present is the same as the velocity of light.

□ To suggest how electromagnetic waves can propagate.

□ To mention special relativity as an alternative to magnetism.

We saw in Chapter 7 how a changing magnetic field can generate electric field loops, described by Faraday's law. These will cause a charged particle to orbit and induced currents to flow within any metal present. We found also that current, in other words charge flowing, produces loops of magnetic field according to Ampere's law. In Chapter 8 we considered self-induction, where the changing magnetic field set up by a varying current produced an electric field acting against the source of the original current.

You should now be prepared for the idea that electric and magnetic fields might generate each other, an insight first described mathematically by Clerk Maxwell in 1864.

The Time Needed to Establish a Current

As an introduction, we consider a problem described in Chapters 2 and 3, when the instantanous switching of a light was discussed. It was clear that charge carrier speed was not involved, being far too slow, and the question became whether the potential gradient across a conductor was set up instantaneously or only after a certain time.

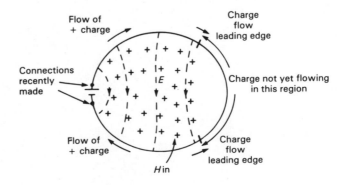

Fig. 11.1   Fields generated while a current is established.

When a battery is connected to a circuit, the positive terminal pulls electrons in and the negative pushes them out, while an electric field is being set up across the capacitance between each side of the circuit, as shown in Fig. 11.1.

Carter, chapter 3, discusses the change in E lines within a circuit when first switched on.

During this process a current is flowing, setting up an H field as shown. The space taken up by the H field increases as the leading edges of the charge flow themselves move round, thus more flux is being made all the time. The rate of increase of this flux generates an e.m.f. which must, by Lenz's law, act against the battery e.m.f. Even if the wire resistance is zero, there will clearly be a limit to how quickly this new flux can be made. Moreover, there is a limit to how slowly: the same limit! If flux is generated slower than sufficient for its e.m.f. to counteract the battery e.m.f., the current will increase and the edges move faster. If more quickly, the current will decrease, slowing the edges. The speed of the charge movement edges is fixed, therefore, by the capacitance, which determines how much charge is needed to set up the E field, and the self-inductance, which determines how much flux is made from a given rate of flow of this charge.

The circuit is being dealt with as a transmission line, but it is still just a circuit!

Consider a small region of circuit, near the pulse edge, shown in Fig. 11.2.

At the point reached by the pulse edge, the two conductors will have a certain capacitance per metre, C_m, and inductance per metre, L_m. The capacitance to be charged when the pulse moves out a distance δx is $C_m \delta x$ and similarly the self-inductance of that same region is $L_m \delta x$.

Obviously for a proper line, such as a coaxial or twin cable, these quantities will apply to their whole length.

Current I required to charge $C_m \delta x$ in time δt is given by:

$$I \delta t = C_m \delta x \mathscr{E}$$

so
$$I = C_m \mathscr{E} \, \delta x / \delta t = C_m \mathscr{E} v \tag{11.1}$$

This current generates flux Φ given by $\Phi = NI/S$ and $S = N^2/L$ where $N = 1$ in each case, so

The H field is effectively generated by just one turn.

$$\delta \Phi = I L_m \delta x$$

Finally, the rate of change of this flux generates an e.m.f. which from the earlier arguments, and ignoring the wire resistance, must be equal to the battery e.m.f. E. Again regarding $N = 1$ and ignoring signs, as the directions have been argued intuitively:

$$\mathscr{E} = \delta \Phi / \delta t = I L_m \delta x / \delta t = L_m I v \tag{11.2}$$

Combining Eqns (11.1) and (11.2), I and $\mathscr{E}$ both cancel, leaving:

$$v = 1/\sqrt{(L_m C_m)} \tag{11.3}$$

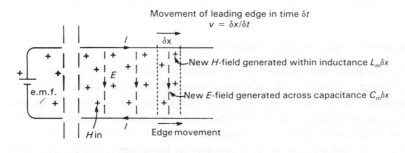

Movement of leading edge in time δt
$v = \delta x / \delta t$

New H-field generated within inductance $L_m \delta x$

New E-field generated across capacitance $C_m \delta x$

Edge movement

Fig. 11.2 Detail of the leading edge of a current pulse.

See Carter, chapter 7, for example.

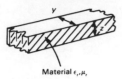

Material ϵ_r, μ_r

So the speed of an electrical pulse edge can be easily related to the inductance and capacitance per metre of the circuit. It would appear that complex calculations are needed for any particular geometry, but instead a remarkably simple result can be found instead. Unfortunately, to prove it generally requires mathematics we have not yet dealt with, but two examples will illustrate what happens.

In Chapter 8 we found the capacitance per metre and inductance per metre of a printed board track, and arrived at an estimate of:

$$C_m = \frac{\epsilon_0 \epsilon_r y}{z}, \qquad L_m = \frac{\mu_0 \mu_r z}{y}$$

$$\text{Thus speed } v = 1 \Big/ \sqrt{\left(\frac{\epsilon_0 \epsilon_r y}{z} \times \frac{\mu_0 \mu_r z}{y} \right)} = 1/\sqrt{(\mu_0 \mu_r \epsilon_0 \epsilon_r)} \qquad (11.4)$$

The importance of this equation is not what appears in it, but what has vanished! There are no geometrical factors at all.

However, the values of C_m and L_m depended on some very dubious assumptions about the shape of E lines and the reluctance of the space, so perhaps in this simple case some subtle factors were lost.

A safer example would be a coaxial cable, where both E and H fields are safely confined and symmetrical. In Worked Examples 4.3 and 8.1 we found:

$$C_m = \frac{2\pi \epsilon_0 \epsilon_r}{\ln(r_2/r_1)}, \qquad L_m = \frac{\mu_0 \mu_r \ln(r_2/r_1)}{2\pi}$$

Thus speed V again $= 1/\sqrt{(\mu_0 \mu_r \epsilon_0 \epsilon_r)}$.

Other shapes can be tried, and the remarkable result is always found, that the speed of a pulse depends only on the universal constants μ_0 and ϵ_0 and the material constant μ_r and ϵ_r and not on the geometry.

This can be readily confirmed by experiment also.

This has several consequences:

(a) When considering pulse delays in high-speed systems, only path lengths and surrounding materials need be considered, not the detailed geometry.
(b) Cables can be designed very simply to produce particular delays.
(c) The geometrical factors in C_m will always be the reciprocal of those in L_m.
(d) Pulse speed in a vacuum, $1/\sqrt{(\mu_0 \epsilon_0)}$, must be regarded as a universal constant.

Experiments show that $1/\sqrt{(v_0 \epsilon_0)}$ is numerically equal to the velocity of light, approximately 3×10^8 ms^{-1}. This was first shown by Maxwell and led him to predict that light is an electromagnetic wave. This led in turn to the experiments of Hertz, in which he produced radio waves and made 'wireless' communication possible.

Characteristic impedance of a transmission line

Before we leave pulses within circuits, we note that the current I that flowed while the fields were growing had nothing whatever to do with circuit resistance, which was assumed to be zero anyway, and everything to do with inductance and capacitance. While the fields were being set up, the circuit behaved to the battery as if it had a resistance equal to $\mathscr{E}/I$, regardless of what ohmic resistance it may really have had. This value is called the **characteristic impedance**, and clearly applies only for the period while the fields are being set up. In practice this means it is only important for 'long, thin circuits' such as signal cables and power lines, which are called **transmission lines**.

The characteristic impedance, Z_0, of a line whose properties are described above is found by substituting Eqn(11.3) in Eqn(11.1):

$$I = C_m \mathscr{E}/\sqrt{(L_m C_m)}$$
$$\text{so} \quad Z_0 = \mathscr{E}/I = \sqrt{(L_m/C_m)} \tag{11.5}$$

Or in Eqn(11.2) of course.

It can be shown that maximum power is transferred from a source into a circuit whose impedance is the same as that of the source. Hence for efficient signal transmission, signal sources are impedance-matched to their transmission lines and the lines are matched at the other end to the input of the receiving circuit.

This also avoids signal reflection, as Carter, chapter 7, explains.

Cables to a specification called uniradio no.M202 have a characteristic impedance of 75Ω and a capacitance of 56 pF m^{-1}. Determine the speed of pulses down such a cable and the relative permittivity required of the insulation, assuming it is non-magnetic. (Answer: Speed = 2.4×10^8 m s^{-1}; relative permittivity 1.56)

Exercise 11.1

Electromagnetic Waves

Eqn(11.4) was remarkable in containing no geometrical factors. Could it even be asked whether actual circuit components are necessary? From what you know so far from this book, the answer ought to be 'yes', because the only way we know to make a magnetic field is by using a current.

Displacement current

Maxwell had just this problem and invented a quantity called **displacement current** to overcome it. He could not demonstrate its existence, and in a sense Hertz's manufacture of radio waves was a proof of displacement current rather than a verification of Maxwell's mathematics, which any good theorist could have carried out. We have the benefit of hindsight and can argue for displacement current experimentally.

Consider an a.c. circuit containing a capacitor. A Rogowski spiral around the circuit registers an H field, even though current is flowing only in the actual wires and there is no complete circuit. The spiral still detects a field even if it is placed to surround the capacitor. Clearly, the space surrounding the capacitor is 'fooled' into thinking there is an actual current flowing, when really there is only a changing D field produced by charge moving on and off the plates.

Now as $Q = \iint D.dA$, from Eqn(4.3) and $I = dQ/dt$, the current equivalent of the changing field in the capacitor, the displacement current I_D is given by

$$I_D = \frac{\partial}{\partial t} \iint D.dA \tag{11.6}$$

As a conduction current I_C may also be present, equal to $\iint J.dA$, the complete version of Ampere's law may now be written as:

$$\oint H.dl = \iint (J + \partial D/\partial t).dA \tag{11.7}$$

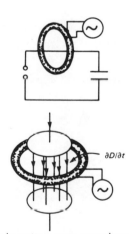

$\partial D/\partial t$

This is not an easy experiment to carry out, as a substantial current at several tens of kilohertz is required. It is also difficult to separate electrostatic effects from the desired electromagnetic induction.

This can be differentiated to give curl $H = J + \partial D/\partial t$, as explained in Carter, chapter 8. Conductors complicate the situation, because of the J term in Eqn(11.7).

Maxwell's equations

Eqns (4.3), (7.5), (7.7) and (11.7) are known as Maxwell's equations, and can be combined mathematically to predict waves that travel at a speed given by $1/\sqrt{(\mu_0 \mu_r \epsilon_0 \epsilon_r)}$ independent of any conductors.

These are listed in Carter, chapter 8.

Unfortunately, the mathematics is not easy, and in any case is best approached from the differential forms of these equations, which have been given as marginal notes near each one.

For this book, an attempt will be made to show how the general idea of waves follows from the equations, without detailed analysis. Be warned, this is a very simple model, and involves more arm-waving than genuine analysis! Even so, the author hopes that the seeds of understanding will have been sown, to bear fruit in later study.

We consider the case if the circuit in Fig. 11.2 is not complete, and ask what happens when a series of pulses reaches the end.

In Fig. 11.2, a pulse edge travels down the circuit, making an E field down and an H field in, on the diagram. If the circuit were driven not by a battery but by an oscillator, the direction of the current, though not of the pulse edge, would be continually reversed, as in Fig. 11.3(a), where the edge is approaching a broken end of the circuit.

This ignores retarded potentials, near and far fields and all sorts of subtleties. It really is only a first look.

When the pulse edge reaches the end, the point x will experience an increasing value of both D (from E) and B (from H), followed by a decreasing value of both, and so on. From Ampere's and Faraday's laws respectively, the dD/dt will generate a loop of H, while the dB/dt will generate a loop of E, beyond the end of the circuit as shown in Fig. 11.3(b). For any point such as y just beyond the loops, the situation will be exactly as at x previously; E and H will be changing and will generate a new pair of loops, propagating the electromagnetic wave out into space.

Though the picture is crude and incomplete, it allows us to see intuitively several important aspects of electromagnetic wave behaviour;

(a) If you sit at a point watching waves go past, the E field and B field will both be a maximum at the same time.

(b) The E field and B field are at right angles to each other, and to the direction of wave propagation.

(c) The fields maintain their direction, defining a plane of polarization of the electromagnetic wave.

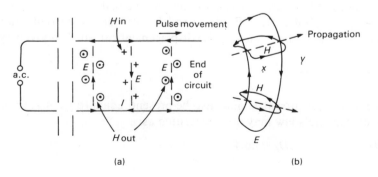

Fig. 11.3 Propagation of electromagnetic waves from the end of a line.

Polarization of light and liquid crystals

Light is polarized in the same way as radio waves. Certain materials allow through only one direction of polarization and yet others rotate the plane of polarization of light passing through. A liquid crystal has the latter property. If a thickness is chosen to rotate the plane through 90° then it will allow the transmission of light through 'crossed polaroids'. An electric field temporarily removes this ability and no light gets through when a field is applied, therefore. So a liquid crystal cell has an opacity controlled by an electric field, and is used in displays as described in Chapter 5.

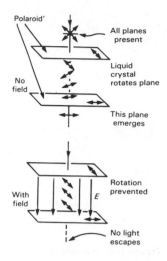

Electromagnetism and Relativity

The close relationship between electric and magnetic fields and the velocity of light should now be clear. The velocity of light itself has one remarkable property, discovered in the late nineteenth century and used by Einstein in his invention of relativity, which led to an alternative picture of magnetism.

Michelson and Morley were attempting to find the speed of the earth through a material called the aether, which was thought to bear the same relation to light as air does to sound waves. The American scientists measured the speed of light, c, in two directions at right angles on two occasions six months apart. To their amazement the answers were always the same.

Proposals were made to allow the earth to sweep the aether along with it, or to assume that objects moving through the aether are shortened by exactly the amount to give the same answer to all c measurements, but Einstein saw a simpler yet more revolutionary answer.

Instead of inventing mechanisms to make c values look the same when they should not be, why not assume they always are the same, to any observer, and start from there? He went on to consider measurements by accelerating observers, in his General Theory of Relativity, but the Special Theory, where only steady speeds are involved, is sufficient for our needs here.

This could be the starting point of a whole book, rather than the last chapter, so we will select one result of the constancy of c to any observer, and apply it briefly to just one illustrative example.

Unless the earth were, by chance, stationary, different readings would be obtained from two experiments at right angles. As the earth moves in its orbit at about 30 km s^{-1}, repeating the work after six months would have solved this. For a detailed account see Feynman, vol. I.

Time dilation

If someone moves at a steady speed relative to you, it turns out that each of you thinks the other's clock is running slow. Consider observer B in the marginal figure watching a spaceship containing observer A, moving at speed v across B's path. A and B measure the time a pulse of light takes to travel across the width s of A's ship, from x to y. A finds it takes a time t_A, but according to B the pulse travelled from x to z and therefore a longer time t_B is recorded, as c is the same for both observers. When they compare results, B concludes that A's clock is running slow, by a factor of:

$$c/\sqrt{(c^2 + v^2)}$$
$$= 1/\sqrt{(1 + v^2/c^2)}$$

If B carried out a similar experiment, watched by A, A would accuse B of having a slow clock.

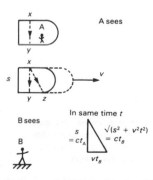

This was the factor involved in deciding whether Eqn (3.15) would apply or not. See the beginning of the section on electron streams. These ideas have been verified by measurements on fast-moving, short-lived particles.

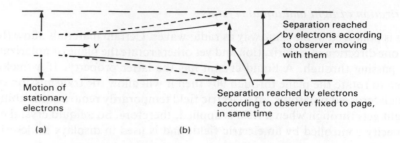

Fig. 11.4 Two views of separating electrons.

The two-electron problem

Although this example is conceptually easy, its maths is more complicated than might be guessed. Duffin gives an example with a more straightforward calculation in chapter 13. See also Carter, chapter 4.

Consider a pair of electrons released close together and stationary relative to an observer. Because of electrostatic repulsion, they begin to move apart, and will reach a certain separation after time t, as shown in Fig. 11.4(a).

If the electrons are now moving at a speed v past the observer, as in Fig. 11.4(b), then to themselves, or an observer moving with them, nothing has changed and they still reach the same separation after time t on their clock. But to an observer who is a relativist, the electrons will have a slow clock and will therefore reach a smaller separation after this observer's time t.

However, another observer could say that this has nothing to do with relativity. The two electrons moving are a pair of electric currents and therefore attract, so the electrostatic repulsion is partly counteracted by a magnetic attraction. Who is right?

Of course they both are. We have returned to our starting point in Chapter 1. Electric and magnetic fields, and perhaps relativity also, are simply models to allow us to explain and connect observations and make useful predictions. As long as a model is self-consistent and fits experimental results it is correct. A particular model may be better for some examples than others, and it is a matter of judgment which to use. The popularity of magnetic fields, as discussed in Chapter 1, is because their concepts and mathematics are simple compared with relativity.

Final Comments

You will inevitably meet other versions of the ideas unfolded in this book. Keep a flexible mind in your studies, so you can see the overall pattern of field theory, even if starting in a different place, or using E and B only or however else an author or lecturer decides is best in a particular context.

The author's school Physics teacher frequently used the term 'puzzle it out' for this necessary hard work.

Above all, make the ideas your own. Think through them until it feels as if you invented them yourself. There are many ways to develop field theory, but only one path to understanding it.

Summary

Pulse speed v in a transmission line of capacitance per unit length C_m and inductance per unit length L_m is given by:

142

$$v = 1/\sqrt{(L_m C_m)}$$

Also $v = 1/\sqrt{(\mu_0 \mu_r \epsilon_0 \epsilon_r)}$ and this is independent of the geometry of the line. The equation applies to free waves in a non-conducting medium also.

The characteristic impedance, Z_0, of a transmission line is given by $Z_0 = (L_m/C_m)$.

Because c is a constant for all observers, an observer watching a moving clock thinks it is running slow. Ths can be used as an alternative explanation of magnetism, though it is rarely used in engineering applications.

The Fundamental Rules of Electromagnetism

1. Lorentz's equation: $\qquad\qquad F = q(E + (v \times B))$

   The next four are Maxwell's equations

2. Gauss' law: $\qquad\qquad\qquad \oint D.dA = Q$

3. Continuity of magnetic flux: $\quad \oint B.dA = 0$

4. Faraday's law: $\qquad\qquad\quad \oint E.dl = -\dfrac{\partial}{\partial t} \iint B.dA$

5. Ampere's law: $\qquad\qquad\quad \oint H.dl = \iint (J + d\,D/dt).dA$

6. E and B fields obey superposition, D and H only in linear media.

7. Changes in electromagnetic systems always act against the causes of those changes.

These can be found in any book, though $\mathscr{E}_0 E$ may be used for D and B/μ_0 for H.

This is Lenz's law and is already in 4 as the minus sign. It is worth remembering even so, as a useful intuitive guide.

Appendix A Brief Note on Integration

It is important to realize that there are two distinct aspects of integration, and unnecessary difficulties often arise because they are confused.

(a) Integration is a description of, or a way of expressing, kinds of problem very common in field theory (and elsewhere), where products are made and then added up.

(b) Having expressed a problem as an integration, there are often standard methods for working it out.

Inevitably, most students spend far longer on aspect (b) than on (a), because of the degree of practice required to become competent. However, the ability to define a problem in terms of integration is a vital skill, and capable of being appreciated quite independently of any facility for 'doing' integrals. Often, students are frightened by an integral sign simply because they are not very good at solving problems. This fear is not necessary! Many, if not most, real problems in integration are not soluble by analytical techniques in any case, and require numerical methods via a computer.

As an example, we will look closely at the idea of charge as an integral.

If a steady current I flows for a time t, the charge passed is by definition equal to It. If I is changing, t will need to be subdivided into units δt so small that during each one I can be regarded as of constant value I_t. The charge passed in time δt is thus $I_t \delta t$. The total charge passed between times t_1 and t_2 is found by adding up all the quantities like $I_t \delta t$ occurring in the larger time interval $t_2 - t_1$.

Without knowing anything further about the problem we can write:

$$\text{charge } Q = \sum_{t_1}^{t_2} I_t \delta t$$

where Σ (sigma) represents the process of adding up the product for every small time interval δt within the larger interval, in other words $\Sigma \delta t = t_2 - t_1$.

If the relationship between I and t is known, for instance it could be sinusoidal so $I = I_o \sin \omega t$, we can shrink δt to an infinitesimal dt, and replace the Σ by a long S called the integral sign:

$$Q = \int_{t_1}^{t_2} I(t)dt \quad \text{or, simply,} \quad \int_{t_1}^{t_2} I \, dt$$

So charge passed is described as 'the time integral of current' or even, loosely, as 'integrated current'.

If I is a continuous function of time, even if unknown, Q is expressed as an integral even if in real life it would be estimated by a numerical process.

If $\int I(t)dt$ is soluble analytically, the operation can then be carried out using standard techniques.

As a further example, energy, W, is related to power, P, by $W = \int P dt$.

Line and surface integrals are specified in exactly the same way, as the derivations of Eqns(3.12) and (2.17) show, though again they are often solved

If *I* occurs in pulses at specified intervals it is called a discrete variable and the Σ notation would be used. See books on signal processing.

144

numerically. For surface integrals the sign is often, as in this book, written double to illustrate that two dimensions are involved and therefore the actual calculation may need to be performed in two stages. However, this is not essential, and often books use a single integral sign for all integrations.

For methods of carrying out integration, many books are available, but remember an engineer's job may cease once the problem has been specified as an integral. That is the important task.

For example Stroud.

Answers to Problems

(b) When rod rotated N times, point on track moves L along, so length is hypotenuse of Δ whose other sides are L and $2\pi rN$. Total width $L - Nd$ so divide by N for width of track, hence number of squares.

Note reasonable linearization.

Hence calculate voltages at junctions on either side of meter.

Surface temperature will clearly increase with power density.

0.2 μm may be the mean free path, but a few will travel much further — these are the ones which will cause ionization.

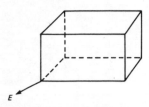

You could call it 20% of the actual value — it's a moot point!
If the lower plate is of equal and opposite potential there is a zero equipotential surface halfway between the plates.

This is an enormous force on particles of mass 1.6×10^{-27} kg. Ignoring relativity, such a force would accelerate them to the speed of light in less than the radius of an atom! This is a hint of the size of the 'strong' nuclear force that binds protons in atomic nuclei.

Remember to use the r.m.s. value of $\mathcal{E}$ for part (b).

2.1 (a) Simply apply Eqn(2.20).
    (c) Resistance per square $10^{-6}/0.02 \times 10^{-6} = 50\ \Omega$.
    So 10 kΩ = 50 × number of squares in track; hence $N = 62$.

2.2 e.g. 0°C, 2 μA; 10°C, 21 μA; 20°C, 44 μA; 30°C, 59 μA.

2.3 (b) e.g. for graph 2, R 1 MΩ at -70°C, 10 kΩ at 5°C.
    Substituting in exponential equation gives $B = 3500$ K.

2.4 (a) 1000 Ω; (b) Resistance of strained gauges 987 Ω, current through meter 52.4 μA.

3.1 Units A m^{-2} × V m^{-1} = W m^{-3}; (a) 2.1×10^5 W m^{-3}; (b) 10^9 W m^{-3}; (c) 1.3×10^{12} W m^{-3}.

3.2 8600 V.

3.3 Distance 4 μm.

3.4 (a) Voltage gradient in each direction same along each edge.
    (b) Up 30 V mm^{-1}; right 6 V mm^{-1}; out 120 V mm^{-1}. Resultant E 124 V mm^{-1} magnitude, 76° to EA, 87° to DA, 14.6° to BA — see Fig. 3.12 and margin.

4.1 (a) -0.74 nC; (b) 25 V.

4.2 1 mV.

4.3 25%.

4.4 12.5%.

4.5 (b) Call $x = B \sin \omega t$ and substitute in answer to (a): $I = V dC/dt$ so $\propto \sin 2\omega t$.

4.6 (a) (i) 348 pF; (ii) 179 pF; (b) 3.2 V.

4.8 (a) 3×10^6 V; (b) 6.25 μA.

4.9 (a) 14.8 pF; (b) 59.3 pF (flux lines outside as well as between); (c) 103.6 pF; 148.1 pF.

5.1 (a) 1800 MV; (b) 1010 MJ; (c) 13.5×10^{12} W.

5.2 (a) 2×10^{-5} C m^{-2}; (b) 45 mN.

5.3 (a) e (i.e. 2.718...); (b) 2.06 MV.

5.4 (a) 1106 pF; (b) 553 pF; (c) 0.277 μC; (d) 11.75 mN; (e) 11.75 N m^{-1}; (f) 18.2 N m^{-1}.

5.5 2.3 N.

6.1 (a) 1.99×10^5 H^{-1}; (b) 1.68 Wb s^{-1}; (c) 7140 turns.

6.2 (a) 2.213×10^8 H^{-1}; (b) 2.122×10^6 H^{-1}; (c) 80 μC; (d) 5.4 V.

7.1 0.2 N.

7.2 (a) $\mathcal{E} = 0.0316 \sin$ (or cos) $126t$; (b) 12.6 W.

7.4 (a) $H = \dfrac{I}{4\pi r}\left(\dfrac{l}{\sqrt{(r^2 + l^2)}} + \dfrac{L - l}{\sqrt{(r^2 + (L - l)^2)}}\right)$; see marginal figure for rectangle, for which

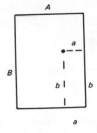

$$H = \dfrac{I}{4\pi}\left(\dfrac{a}{b\sqrt{(b^2 + a^2)}} + \dfrac{A - a}{b\sqrt{(b^2 + (A - a)^2)}} + \dfrac{b}{a\sqrt{(a^2 + b^2)}} + \dfrac{B - b}{a\sqrt{(a^2 + (B - b)^2)}}\right).$$

(b) $H = NI/2a$; (c) $H = NI\sin^3\alpha/2a$;

(d) $H = NI(\sin\alpha_2 - \sin\alpha_1)$, leading to $H = nI$, where n is turns metre^{-1}, when $\alpha_1 \to 0$, $\alpha_2 \to 180°$.

8.1 (a) Ratio $(S \text{ in } b)/(S \text{ in } a)$ 1.09; (b) S 2.12×10^5 H^{-1};
(c) L 10.6 H, M 0.35 H.

8.2 x 0.148 m, N 377, thickness 6.7 mm, resistance 0.027 Ω.

8.3 C −ve relative to D, E +ve relative to F.

8.4 (a) μ_r 5170, L 65 mH; (b) appr 70 mH, 8 mH, 0.8 mH (take gradients for small-signal inductance); (c) appr 4 mH in all cases (core reluctance ≪ gap reluctance as max B appr 0.12 T).

9.1 75 W.

9.2 1290 N.

9.3 9.4 mm.

9.4 (a) assuming radial flux, S 4.34×10^6 H^{-1}; (b) B 83 mT;
(c) 4.5 μN m.

10.1 80000 V m^{-1}.

10.2 (a) B 34.3 mT; (b) n 2.86×10^{19} m^{-3}, μ 0.116 m^2 V^{-1} s^{-1}, p-type.

10.3 (a) S 4.88×10^6 H^{-1}; (b) B 0.57 T; (c) 5.6 mA, 77.6 mV; (d) 4.5%.

10.4 (a) around 90 kV!; (b) 14.3 mT; (c) 226 mA; (d) 177 mH; (e) 0.498 mH;
(f) L_s 3.15 mH, $N_1:N_2:N_3$ 1:6.33:355.

Bibliography

Book Referred to Frequently

Carter, R.G.: *Electromagnetism for Electronic Engineers*; Van Nostrand Reinhold, Wokingham.
Duffin, W.J.: *Electricity and Magnetism*; McGraw-Hill, Maidenhead.
Horowitz, P. and Hill, W.: *The Art of Electronics*; Cambridge University Press, Cambridge.
Solymar, L. and Walsh, D.: *Lectures on the Electrical Properties of Materials*; Oxford University Press, Oxford.
Yorke, R.: *Electric Circuit Theory*, Pergamon, Oxford.

Books Referred to Occasionally

Bennett, G.A.G.: *Electricity and Modern Physics*; Arnold, London.
Bolton, B.: *Electromagnetism*; Van Nostrand Reinhold, Wokingham.
Caro, D.E., McDonell, J.A. and Spicer, B.M.: *Modern Physics*; Arnold, London.
Escher, M.C.: *The Graphic Work of M.C. Escher*; McDonald, London.
Feynman, R.P. *et al*: *The Feynman Lectures on Physics* (3 vols); Addison–Wesley, London.
Fink, D.G. and Beaty, H.W.: *Standard Handbook for Electrical Engineers*; McGraw-Hill, Maidenhead.
Grossner, N.R.: *Transformers for Electronic Circuits*; McGraw-Hill, Maidenhead.
Laithwaite, E.R.: *Exciting Electrical Machines*; Pergamon, Oxford.
Loveday, G.C.: *Electronic Testing and Fault Diagnosis*; Pitman, London.
Nuffield A-Level Physics Teacher's Guides 2,3,7,8 or *Revised Nuffield A-Level Physics Student's Guide* (in two parts); Longmans, Harlow.
Oatley, C.W.: *Electric and Magnetic Fields*; Cambridge University Press, Cambridge.
Ritchie, G.J.: *Transistor Circuit Techniques*; Van Nostrand Reinhold, Wokingham.
Stroud, K.A.: *Engineering Mathematics*; Macmillan, London.
Wilson, J. and Hawkes, J.F.B.: *Optoelectronics*; Prentice-Hall, London.
Wiring Regulations (15th edition); IEE, London.

Other Useful Books

Symbols and Abbreviations; IEE, London.
Any O or A Level Physics textbook.

Index

'Summary' references are not given. m means marginal note. * means diagram or picture.

acceleration of electrons, 33, 44, 126
actuator, 109–10
air gaps in magnetic circuits, 73–4
ampere A, definition, 5, 115
Ampère's law, 85–7, 139, 143
  and permanent magnets, 113
area as vector, 9–10
avalanche ionization, 12–13, 33–4, 54

B field, 77–80
  in long solenoid, 88
  in short solenoid, 91
  near wire, 88–9
  of current element, 88
B–H curve, 97–100, *98–9
  energy losses, 109
bacteria tails, 61
bias signal in magnetic recording, 113m
Biot–Savart equation, 89
bounce, switch, 123
bubbles, magnetic, 104

cadmium sulphide (CdS), 28
calculations,
  electrostatics, 45, *45, 53
  magnetism, 95
camera tube, TV, 131, *131
capacitance C, 36–7
  current 'through', 44m, 63, 139
  effect of dielectric, 42, 50, 63
  form of equations, 46m
  slope, 37m, 48
capacitors, 36
  applications, 63
  charging and discharging, 36–7
  design, 63–4
  energy of, 57–8
  in series and in parallel, 44–5
  parallel-plate, 41–2
  structure, 64, *65
  variable, 53
car ignition, 75
cathode ray tube,
  oscilloscope, 127, 131, *129
  TV/VDU, 127, 131, *130, 134
cavity,
  within a conductor, 42
  within a ferromagnetic material, 113

characteristic impedance, 138
charge Q, 5
  carrier, 26–7, 120
  concentration (number), 121, 2
  connection with current, 5, 23, 37, 44, 144
  density (volume), 6
  density (surface), 38–9
  distribution time, 50m
  drift velocity, 6, 33
    in wire, 6, 13
    in semiconductor, 27
  electrostatic force on, 59, 119
  interactions, 4
  mobility μ, 26, 27–8, 121
  positive and negative, 4–5
  'storage' in a capacitor, 36
chord value of μ_r, 98m
circuit breakers, 110
circular path of electron in field, 80, 83, 127
clamp meter (clip-on ammeter), 124–5, *124, 133
CMOS logic, power loss, 58m
coaxial cable, *32, 43, 69
  capacitance, 45–6
  inductance, 95–6
  leakage current, 32
coefficient,
  of mutual inductance, 93
  of self inductance, 92
  temperature, 13, 15, 18
coercivity, 98
coil, torque on, 114
compass, 71m, 81
conductance G, 7
conduction,
  equations, 7, 26
  in gases, 12, 33–4
  in liquid, 12
  in metals, 13, 21, *21
  in non-metals, 13
conductivity, 7, 26
  effect of temperature, 12–13, 15
  effect of strain, 16
conductor in electrostatic field, 42, 44, 51
conservative field, 29, 32
constant,
  electric ϵ_o, 41
  magnetic μ_o, 73, 85, 116

cores, transformer and inductor, 99, 100, 102–4
corona discharge, 65m, 66
coulomb C, 5
Coulomb, C. A., 5m, 56m
Coulomb's law, 56m
coupling coefficient, 101
cross product of vectors, 78, 80, 89, 115m
curl, 83m, 87m, 139m
current I, 5
  displacement dD/dt, 139
  element, B field near, 88–9
  time to set up, 136–8
cyclotron frequency, 128m

depletion zone, 48
dielectric, 50
  fields in and near, 51–2
  strength, 54, 63–4
diode, semiconductor junction, 48
dipole,
  electrostatic, 56
  aerial, 89m
discharge, gas, 12, 33–4
  prevention, 55
displacement current dD/dt, 139
div, 40m, 79m
domain theory of magnetization, 99, *99
door, magnetic sensor, 75, *75
doping, 13m
dot product of vectors, 10, 31, 40, 79, 85
dust precipitator, 35, 65
dynamic equilibrium, 12, 34
dynamo effect, 83–4

earth, 26, *26, 50
  leakage circuit breaker (trip), 111m
eddy currents, 83, 100
edge effects, 30
Einstein, A., 141
electret, 54
electric,
  constant ϵ_o, 41
  field E, 23
    connected with potential gradient, 24
    energy of, 59
electrolytes, 5m, 13
electromagnetic,

induction, 70
waves, 89m, 139
electromotive force (e.m.f.), 6
electron, 4
  deflection,
    electrostatic, 126
    magnetic, 127
  emission,
    field, 125
    photo-, 125, 131
    secondary, 125, 132
  focusing, 11
    axial magnetic, 128, *129
    electrostatic, 128
  free, 33, 125
    acceleration, 33, 126
  gas, 13m
  gun, 11, 126
  -hole pair (FHP), 28, 54
  size of charge q_e, 4
  -volt, 125
electrostatic,
  conditions, 28-9
  induction, 42
  loudspeaker, 53, 61-2, 69
  microphone, *54, 67
electrostriction, 53m
energy,
  and power, 144
  gap E_g, 13, 28
  in charged capacitor, 57-8
  in electric field, 58-9
  in inductance, 107-8
  in magnetic circuit, 108
  in magnetic field, 108
  kinetic, 33
  loss in resistance, 100
  lost when capacitor charged, 58
  of charge W, 6, 57
  of ionization, 12, 34, 35
equilibrium, dynamic, 12, 34
equipotential surfaces,
  electrical, 24-6, 30, 54-5
    of conductor, 42
  magnetic scalar, 86
Escher, M.C., 82m

farad F, 37
Faraday, M., 37m
Faraday cage, 43
Faraday's law, 70, 83, 143
ferrimagnetics, 97
ferrites, 97m, 99, 100, 104
ferromagnetics, 72, 97
field,
  conservative, 28-9
  emission, 125
  lines, electrical, 24-6
  magnetic, 70
  patterns, electrical, 24-6, *25, *30, *41
flame probe, 30
fluorescent lighting, 33-4
flux,
  current I, 8-9
    relation to J, 9

electric Q, 39
magnetic Φ, 70
density,
  current J, 9
  electric D, 39
  magnetic B, 79
lines,
  current, 9
  magnetic, 71
force,
  electrostatic, 59
  from energy change, 59-61, 109
  Lorentz, 119, 143
  magnetic on wire, 77
    on particle, 80
  reluctance, 109
  sensors, 53
Franklin, B., 4m
free electron, 33, 125
frequency response, CRT, 131
fundamental charged particles, 4
fuses, 110

gaps in magnetic circuits, 73-4
garnet, 104
gas,
  discharge and conduction in, 12, 33-4
  electron, 18m
gauge factor, 16
Gauss' law, 39, 46, 143, *40
generator, electrostatic, 48
  Van der Graaf, 48m
grad, 24m
grain size and magnetic properties, 99-100
gravitational field, 23-4, 29

H field, 85, 88
Hall effect, 5, 84, 119, 133
  ammeter, 124, *124, 133
  coefficient, 122
  field, 120
  materials, 27, 121-2
  switches, 123, *123
  voltage, 120, 123
  wattmeter, 125
hard magnetic materials, 99
Helmholtz coils, 134m
henry, 92
Henry, J., 92m
history of units, 3
hole, 13, 26-7, 120
hysteresis, magnetic, 98, 100
  energy loss, 101, 109
  loop, 98, 114

image intensifier, 131-2, *132
impedance, characteristic, 138-9
indium antimonide (InSb), 28
induced e.m.f. direction, 80-2
inductance and reluctance, 93-4, 96, 101
induction,
  electrostatic, 42
  motors, 83
inductor, air-cored, 94-5
infrared detectors, 28m

insulation quality, 63-4
insulators,
  liquid, 12
  solid 13, 50-1
integral,
  line, 32, 85
  loop, 32, 82-3, 87
  surface, 10, 40, 79
    closed, 10, 40, 79
integration, setting up, 57m, 144
intensity of magnetization, 97m
intrinsic semiconductor, 120m
inverse,
  cube law for dipole, 56-7
  square law,
    for D, 40-1, *41
    for E, 55
    for force, 56
    test, 43m
  unity law of potential, 56
ion, 12
ion-pair, 12
ionization,
  avalanche, 12-13, 33-4, 54
  by heat, 12
  by radiation, 12
  energy, 12, 34, 35
isolated conductors, 40, 54

keeper, magnet, 114
kinetic energy of electron, 33, 126
Kirchhoff,
  first law, 10
  second law, 32m

lattice, 13
leakage flux, 94m, 101
Lenz' law, 81-2, 92, 143m
light,
  as electromagnetic wave, 140-1
  detectors, 28, *29
  emission from gas discharge, 33-4
  polarization, 140-1
lightning, 5, 43, 69
  conductors, 43, 55
line integral, 32, 85
linearity,
  coil in field, 115
  loudspeaker, 62, 69, 115
  microphone, 67
  recording head, 74, 113
  use of gaps, 74
liquid,
  conduction, 12
  crystal, 141
    display 67, *68
logarithmic plotting, 16m
loop integral, 32, 82-3, 87
Lorentz, H.A., 119m
Lorentz force, 119, 143
losses, copper and iron, 100m
loudspeaker, electrostatic, 53, 61-2, 69
  moving coil, 115, *115

machines, electromagnetic, 100-3
  energy losses, 100

magnet,
  permanent, 84m, 88m, 99, 113-4, 117
  poles, 79, 114
magnetic,
  bubbles, 104
  circuit, 72
    energy in 108
    gaps in, 73-4
    breaker (MCB), 110, *111
  constant μ_o, 73, 85, 116
    unit, 73m, 94
  field, 70
    energy in, 108
    measurements, Hall effect, 124
    strength, 77m
  flux Φ, 70
    conservation (continuity), 71-2, 79, 143
    density B, 79
    lines, 71
    patterns, 72, 74, 78-9, 113
  force,
    on wire, 77-8
    on particle, 80, 119, 127
  induction *(B)*, 77m
  materials, 70
    hard, 99
    soft, 98
moment per unit volume, 97m
  polarization 97
  scalar potential, 84-86
    gradient H, 85
magnetization, 70, 97
magnetizing force, 85m
magnetomotive force (m.m.f.), 72, 86-7
  gradient, 85m
Maxwell, J.C., 136, 139
Maxwell's equations, 140, 143
mean free path, 34, 35
meter, moving-coil, 115
mho, 7
Michelson–Morley experiment, 141
microphone, electrostatic, *54, 67
  electret, 54, *54
mobility of charge μ, 26-7, 121
models, 2, 12, 21, 50, 52m
motor effect, 77, 83, 114
mutual inductance, 93

n-type semiconductor, 120, 133
neutron, 4m
non-conservative field, 82-3, 87-8
non-spherical charged object, 54-5

ohm, 7
Ohm's equation, 7, 26
  at a point, 26
Ohm's law, 7
ohmic materials, 7
optical filter, electrostatic, 59-60, *60
orbital time for electron, 128
order of topics, 3
oscillators, use of crystals, 53-4
oscilloscope tube, 127, *129, 131

p-type semiconductor, 133
parallel-plate capacitor, 41

particle, magnetic force on, 80, 119, 127
permanent magnet, 84m, 88m, 99, 113-4
permeability, relative μ_r, 73, 97
permittivity, relative ϵ_r, 41
phosphor protection in CRT, 131m, 134
photo-,
  conduction, 27-8, *29, 125m, 131
  copying, 66, *66
  electric effect, photoemission, 125, 131
  multiplier principle, 132m
piezo-,
  electricity, 53
  resistance, 17
plasma, 34
platinum resistance thermometer, 15
polarization,
  charges, 50-1
  magnetic, 97
  of light, 141
  vector P, 52
'Polaroid', 141
poles of magnet, 79, 114
potential, 20-1, *20
  difference, 20-1, 31
  divider rule, 23
  gradient,
    electrical,
      across dielectric, 51-2
      as vector, 24
      connected with field, 24
      in space, 28, *30
      in wire, *25, 24-5
    gravitational, 24
      connected with force, 24
  gravitational 24
  magnetic scalar, 84-6
  model, 20-1, *21
power, electrical P, 6
  density, 35
printed board C and L, 96-7
proximity detector, 124, *123
pulse speed, 6m, 22m, 136-8

Q-factor, 102m
quantum,
  electric, 4
  light, 28, 34, 125

record/playback heads, 74, 113, *113
record-player pickup, 54
relative,
  permeability μ_r, 73, 97
  permittivity ϵ_r, 41
relativity, 3, 141-2
  and magnetism, 142
reluctance S, 72
  force, 109
  measurement, 72m
  minimization, 111-3, 115m
  of air-cored inductor, 94-5
  related to inductance, 93-5, 101
  unit, 93-4
remanence, 98m
residual current circuit breaker, *111, 111, *112
resistance R, 7

per square, 18
  source, 6m
  thermometer, 15, *15
resistivity, 7
resistors, 13-5, *14
  composition, 14
  film, 14, *14, 18
  thick film, 14m
  wirewound, 15, *14
    non-inductive, 15, 92m
resonance, 96-7
retentivity 98
right hand rule, 81, *81, 88m, 115m
Rogowski spiral, 85-7, 139
root mean square average, 12m
rule, right hand, 81, *81, 88m, 115m

saturation, magnetic, 98, 102-3
  loop, 98-9, 114
scalar product of vectors, 10, 31, 40, 79, 85
scaling effects,
  electrostatic, 61
  magnetic, 102-3, 111m
screening,
  electrostatic, 43
  magnetic, 113
self-inductance, 92, 107-8
semiconductor, 13, 15, 26-7, 48, 120-3
  intrinsic, 120m
  junction diode capacitance, 48
  film research, 122-3, *122
siemens S, 7
silicon, 27, 48
sinusoidal flux, 71
skin effect, 96m
slope,
  capacitance, 37m, 48
  value of μ_r, 73, 98m, 101
soft magnetic materials, 98-9
spark gap, 30
speed of electrical pulse, 6m, 22m, 136-8
  along parallel strips, 138
  general case, 138
  in coaxial cable, 138
sphere, capacitance of, 48-9, 55
storage of charge, 36
strain gauge, 16, *16, 19
  bridge, *19
stray capacitance and inductance, 96
'strip' lighting, 33-4
superposition, 6m, 22, 143
surface acoustic waves (SAW), 54
susceptibility, magnetic, 97m
switch,
  bounce and wear, 123
  damage when capacitor charged, 58
  Hall effect, 123, *123
switches, mechanical, limitations, 123

tachometer, electrostatic, 43, *43
temperature,
  and conductivity, 12, 13, 15, 17m
  coefficient, 13, 15, 18-19
  scales, 15m
terminal voltage, 6
tesla, 78

Tesla, N., 78m
thermionic effect, 125
thermistor, 15–16, *16, 18–19
thermodynamic arguments, 29m, 81–2
thermometer, metal resistance, 15, *15
time,
    dilation, 141
        and electron motion, 142
    to set up current, 6m, 22m, 136–8
torque on coil, 114–5
transducers,
    piezoelectric, 53–4
    resistive, 15–17, 28
transformer, 94, 101, 103–4, *103–4, 134–5
    cores, 99, 100, 103–4
    equations, 94

TV/VDU tube, picture, 127, *130, 131, 134
TV camera tube, 131, *131

ultrasonic devices, 53–4
uncharged material, 4
understanding, 2–3
unit vector, 55–6

vector,
    product,
        scalar, 10, 31, 40, 79, 85
        vector, 78, 80, 89, 115m
    unit, 55–6
vibration transducer, electrostatic,
        48
vidicon, 131, *131

voltage, terminal, 6

wattmeter,
    moving coil, 117–8, *117
    Hall effect, 125
weber, 71
Weber, W., 71m
wire,
    B field near, 88, 89
    magnetic force on, 77–8
    self-inductance, 96
work function ϕ_w, 13m, 125

xerography, 66–7, *66

zener breakdown, 48